Scott Foresman - Addison Wesley
MATH

Daily Cumulative Review
Workbook

Scott Foresman - Addison Wesley

Editorial Offices: Glenview, Illinois • New York, New York
Sales Offices: Reading, Massachusetts • Duluth, Georgia • Glenview, Illinois
Carrollton, Texas • Menlo Park, California

http://www.sf.aw.com

Overview

Daily Cumulative Review Workbook provides a continuous review of skills and concepts from Scott Foresman - Addison Wesley MATH. A Daily Review worksheet is provided for each lesson in the Student Edition.

The first section of each worksheet reviews a key objective from the previous lesson. The second section of each worksheet reviews material covered two lessons prior to the current lesson. The third section provides a Mixed Review of problems from previous lessons or chapters. Lesson references are provided with each exercise in Mixed Review.

Daily Review worksheets for Chapter 1 review key concepts from the previous year as well as from Chapter 1.

The *Daily Cumulative Review* format helps students solidify and retain math skills learned throughout the school year.

ISBN 0-201-36910-9

Copyright © Addison Wesley Longman, Inc.

Printed in the United States of America

7 8 9 10 – PO – 03 02 01

Contents

Name _____

Daily Cumulative Review

Mixed Review *(From Last Year)*

Write the number.

1. four _____   **2.** fifteen _____   **3.** sixty-three _____

Write the number that comes before.

4. _____ 47 48   **5.** _____ 50 51

Circle the shape that is congruent to the first shape.

6.

7.

Add or subtract.

8. 2	4	0	6	4	1
+ 2	+ 3	+ 5	+ 3	+ 4	+ 3

9. 6	7	5	8	4	9
− 3	− 0	− 4	− 2	− 4	− 7

10. 8	1	5	7	9	8
+ 0	+ 6	− 2	+ 2	− 1	− 2

11. 9 ducks are on the pond.
2 ducks fly away.
How many ducks are left?

12. Roger sees 7 boats on the lake.
5 more enter the lake.
How many boats are on the
lake now?

_____   _____

Daily Cumulative Review

Use the pictograph to answer each question. *(Lesson 1-1)*

1. Which dog is the favorite?

_____

2. Which dog had 5 votes?

_____

3. How many more students voted
for Collies than for Dalmations?

_____

Student's Favorite Dogs

Dog	Number Counted
Beagle	🐕 🐕 🐕
Collie	🐕 🐕 🐕 🐕 🐕
Shepherd	🐕 🐕 🐕
Poodle	🐕
Dalmations	🐕 🐕

Each 🐕 = 2 votes

Mixed Review *(From Last Year)*

Find each sum.

4. 8 + 10 + 7 = _____   **5.** 9 + 14 + 12 = _____

6.
```
   2 3        6 5        4 3        3 7        5 6
 + 4 2      + 2 6      + 1 4      + 2 8      + 3 4
```

Write how many tens and ones. Write the number.

7.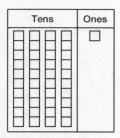

_____ tens _____ ones

_____

8.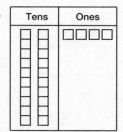

_____ tens _____ ones

_____

9. Carla brought 15 cupcakes for the party. We ate 7 of
them. After that, Barry brought 11 more. How many
cupcakes were there then?

_____ cupcakes

Name _____

Daily Cumulative Review

Use the bar graph to answer each question. *(Lesson 1-2)*

1. Which vegetable was the least favorite? _____

2. Which vegetable received 8 votes?
   _____

3. How many more voted for peas than beans? _____

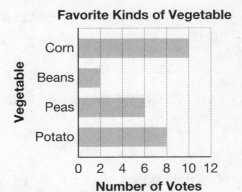

Favorite Kinds of Vegetable

Use the pictograph to answer each question *(Lesson 1-1)*

4. How many students voted for baseball? _____

5. Which activity was voted for the most?
   _____

6. How many symbols would there be if 18 students voted for reading? _____

Student's Favorite Summer Activity

Swimming	☼ ☼ ☼ ☼ ☼
Skating	☼ ☼ ☼
Baseball	☼ ☼ ☼ ☼
Biking	☼ ☼
Reading	☼ ☼ ☼

 = 3 votes

Mixed Review *(From Last Year)*

Write even or odd.

7. 45 _____   **8.** 34 _____   **9.** 26 _____   **10.** 81 _____

Circle the best estimate for the length of each real object.

11.

about 1 inch

about 1 foot

about 1 yard

12.

about 1 inch

about 1 foot

about 1 yard

13. MATH

about 1 inch

about 1 foot

about 1 yard

Name _____

Daily Cumulative Review

Use the line graph to answer each question. *(Lesson 1-3)*

1. In which week did the class collect the most cans?

_____

2. In which week did they collect 75 cans?

_____

3. In which week did they collect 100 cans?

_____

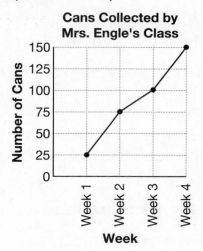

Cans Collected by Mrs. Engle's Class

Use the bar graph to answer each question. *(Lesson 1-2)*

4. Which color received the most votes?

_____

5. Which color had 3 votes?

_____

6. How many students voted for blue?

_____

7. Which colors have less than 9 votes?

_____

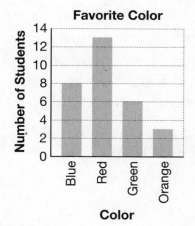

Favorite Color

Mixed Review

Round each number to the nearest ten.

8. 38 _____   **9.** 56 _____   **10.** 73 _____   **11.** 21 _____
(Gr. 2)   *(Gr. 2)*   *(Gr. 2)*   *(Gr. 2)*

12. Jake used 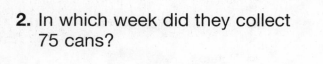 as a symbol to represent 3 students that voted for their
(1-1) favorite subject. Suppose 15 students voted for math. How many symbols would math have?

_____ symbols

Daily Cumulative Review

Use the bar graph to answer each question. *(Lesson 1-4)*

1. How many students all together like baseball or football?

_____

2. How many students voted in all?

_____

3. Which sport had 4 more votes than baseball?

_____

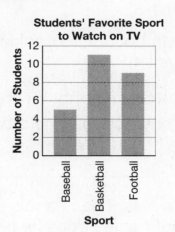

Students' Favorite Sport to Watch on TV

Use the line graph to answer each question. *(Lesson 1-3)*

4. How many books did Mark read in Week 2?

_____

5. In what week did Mark read 2 books?

_____

6. In what week did Mark read the most books?

_____

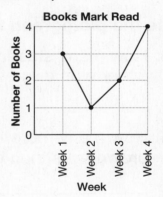

Books Mark Read

Mixed Review

Complete each pattern.

7. 4, 8, 12, _____, _____
(Gr. 2)

8. 15, 12, 9, _____, _____
(Gr. 2)

Use the graph to answer the questions.

9. How many students voted for ice cream?
(1-2)

_____

10. What dessert was the least favorite dessert?
(1-2)

_____

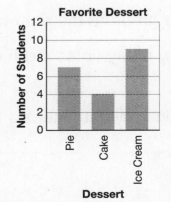

Favorite Dessert

Name _____

Daily Cumulative Review

Write which operation you would use. Then solve.
(Lesson 1-5)

1. Kevin bought 10 cookies. He ate 6 of them. How many cookies did he have left?

   _____

2. Franny bought 8 gold beads and 5 silver beads. How many beads did she buy in all?

   _____

3. Tony has 9 games this season. Tony has played 4 games. How many more games does he have to play?

   _____

Use the pictograph to answer each question. *(Lesson 1-4)*

4. How many students have either blue or green eyes?

   _____

5. How many more students have brown eyes than green eyes?

   _____

6. Which eye color is twice as common as blue eyes?

   _____

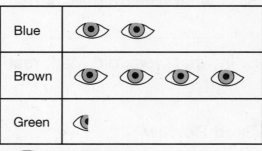

Student's Eye Color

Blue	👁 👁
Brown	👁 👁 👁 👁
Green	👁

👁 = 4 students

Mixed Review

Use the graph at the right to answer the questions.

7. How many votes did the lion get?
   (1-2)

   _____

8. Which animal received the most votes?
   (1-2)

   _____

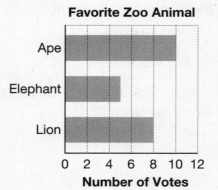

Favorite Zoo Animal

Ape

Elephant

Lion

0 2 4 6 8 10 12
Number of Votes

Daily Cumulative Review

Complete each table. Write the rule for each. *(Lesson 1-6)*

1.

In	3	5	7	9	11	13
Out	7	9	11			

Rule: _____

2.

In	18	17	16	15	14	13
Out	15	14	13			

Rule: _____

Write which operation you would use. Then solve. *(Lesson 1-5)*

3. Janice had 4 CDs. She got 3 more for her birthday. How many CDs does she have now?

_____

4. Chad has $4. He wants to buy a book that costs $8. How much more money does he need?

_____

5. Philip had 10 marbles. He lost 3 on the playground. How many marbles does he have now?

_____

Mixed Review

Write the numbers in order from least to greatest.

6. 56   87   45   _____ _____ _____
(Gr. 2)

7. 67   37   57   _____ _____ _____
(Gr. 2)

8. 64   42   24   _____ _____ _____
(Gr. 2)

Daily Cumulative Review

Complete the tally table. *(Lesson 1-7)*

1. Use the data to help organize the votes. The votes for "Cheese" have already been counted.

Our Favorite Type of Pizza

Type	Tally	Number
Cheese	IIII	
Pepperoni		
Hamburger		
Sausage		

Cheese	Pepperoni	Cheese
Hamburger	Sausage	Cheese
Pepperoni	Sausage	Pepperoni
Pepperoni	Pepperoni	Pepperoni
Cheese	Sausage	Hamburger

Complete each table. Write the rule for each. *(Lesson 1-6)*

2.

In	3	7	12	16	20	24
Out	9	13	18			

Rule: _____

3.

In	11	8	7	5	13	4
Out	16	13	12			

Rule: _____

Mixed Review

Use the bar graph to answer each question.

4. How long did Silvia practice on Wednesday?
(1-2)

_____

5. How long did Silvia practice on Friday?
(1-2)

_____

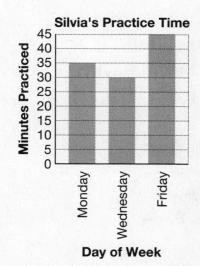

Silvia's Practice Time

Daily Cumulative Review

Complete the pictograph. Use the data in the tally table.
(Lesson 1-8)

1.

Favorite Fruit

Type	Tally
Pears	II
Apples	ⅢⅢ III
Peaches	IIII
Bananas	ⅢⅢ ⅢⅢ II
Oranges	ⅢⅢ ⅢⅢ
Grapes	ⅢⅢ ⅢⅢ III

Favorite Fruit

Pears	■
Apples	
Peaches	
Bananas	
Oranges	
Grapes	

■ = 2 students

2. Suppose each symbol in the pictograph above represented 3 students. How many symbols would there be for "Bananas"? _____

Complete each tally table. *(Lesson 1-7)*

3.

Our Favorite Type of Music

Type	Tally	Number
Country	ⅢⅢ	
Rap	ⅢⅢ I	
Rock	ⅢⅢ ⅢⅢ I	
Classical	II	

4.

Our Favorite Sport

Type	Tally	Number
Baseball		3
Basketball		9
Football	ⅢⅢ	
Soccer	ⅢⅢ II	

Mixed Review

Find each sum.

5. 63 + 11 = _____   44 + 22 = _____   32 + 12 = _____
(Gr. 2)

6. Joe baked 5 dozen cookies in the morning and 4 dozen in the
(1-5) afternoon. How many dozen cookies did he bake that day?

_____

Name _____

Daily Cumulative Review

Use the data in the table to complete the bar graph.
(Lesson 1-9)

1.

Month	Number of Rainy Days
April	15
May	9
June	3
July	7
August	5

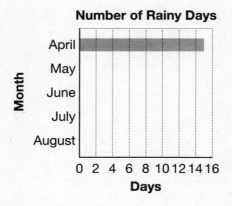

Number of Rainy Days

Complete the pictograph. Use the data in the tally table.
(Lesson 1-8)

2.

Student's Favorite Ice Cream

Chocolate	卌 卌 卌 卌
Strawberry	卌 |||
Vanilla	卌 卌 ||||
Chocolate Swirl	卌 卌 ||

Student's Favorite Ice Cream

Chocolate	● ● ● ● ●
Strawberry	
Vanilla	
Chocolate Swirl	

● = 4 students

Mixed Review

3. Complete the table and write the rule.
(1-6)

In	2	4	6	8	10	12
Out	5	7		11		

Rule: _____

4. Write which operation you would use. Then solve.
(1-5)

John owns 4 frogs and 9 fish. How many pets does John own?

_____

Daily Cumulative Review

Use the data to answer each question. *(Lesson 1-10)*

Your class has taken a survey of the school to find the most popular sandwich. The table shows the kind and number of votes for each sandwich.

Sandwich Choices	
Ham	50
Cheese	45
Peanut Butter and Jelly	80
Ham and Cheese	65

1. Look at the data. Is the information best suited for a bar graph or a pictograph? Explain.

_____

_____

2. What would you title the graph? _____

Use the data in the table to complete the bar graph.
(Lesson 1-9)

3.

Great Places to Picnic	
Lake	6
Ocean	4
Park	10
Backyard	3
Other	2

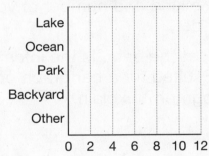

Great Places to Picnic

Mixed Review

Write which operation you would use. Then solve.

4. Marcy walked 3 miles yesterday and 2 miles today. How far did she
   (1-5) walk in the two days?

_____

5. Carson bought 7 packs of baseball cards. He opened 3 of the packs
   (1-5) that day. How many packs does he still have to open?

_____

Name _____

Daily Cumulative Review

Look for a pattern to help you solve each problem.
(Lesson 1-11)

1. If the pattern continues, which shape should come next? _____

2. How many triangles should come next? _____

3. What are the next 3 numbers?

10, 15, 20, _____, _____, _____

Answer each question. *(Lesson 1-10)*

Your class has taken a survey to find the most popular pet. The table shows the kind and number of votes for each pet.

Pet	
Hamster	2
Cat	10
Dog	8
Fish	5
Turtle	1

4. Look at the data. Is the information best suited for a bar graph or a pictograph? Explain.

_____

_____

5. What would you title the graph?

_____

Mixed Review

6. Complete the table. Write the rule.
(1-6)

In	11	13	14	17	23	35
Out	6	8	9			

Rule: _____

Name _____

Daily Cumulative Review

Write each number in standard form. *(Lesson 2-1)*

1. twenty-seven _____

2. sixteen _____

3. four hundred eighty-one _____

4. 300 + 50 + 3 = _____

5. 300 + 3 = _____

Find the next 3 numbers in each pattern. *(Lesson 1-11)*

6. 8, 10, 12, 14, _____, _____, _____

7. 6, 9, 12, 15, _____, _____, _____

8. Cassie and her friends played a game. Cassie picked up 2 jacks, 4 jacks, 8 jacks. Heather continued the pattern. What will she pick up next? _____

Mixed Review

Use the bar graph to answer **9–11**.

9. How many people voted
(1-2) for relays?

_____

10. Which game was voted for
(1-2) the most?

_____

11. How many more people voted
(1-4) for tag than hide & seek?

_____

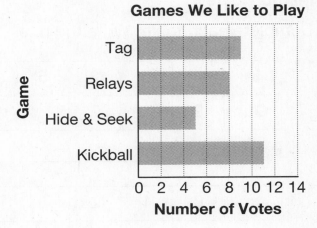

Games We Like to Play

Game — Tag, Relays, Hide & Seek, Kickball

Number of Votes: 0 2 4 6 8 10 12 14

12. Write which operation you would use.
(1-5) Then solve.

Jania is in an 8-mile race. She has run 5 miles already. How many more miles does she need to run?

_____

Name _____

Daily Cumulative Review

Complete the table. *(Lesson 2-2)*

	Number	Number of Ones	Number of Tens	Number of Hundreds
1.	100			
2.	500	500		
3.	700			7
4.	600		60	
5.	300			

Write the word name for each number. *(Lesson 2-1)*

6. 563 _____   **7.** 88 _____

8. 410 _____   **9.** 609 _____

Mixed Review

Complete each table. Write the rule.

10.
(1-6)

In	4	6	2	5	10	8
Out	9	11	7			

Rule: _____

11.
(1-6)

In	0	1	2	3	4	5
Out		5		7		9

Rule: _____

12. If the pattern continues, which shape should come next? _____
(1-11)

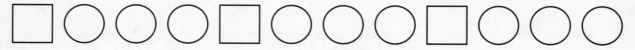

14

Daily Cumulative Review

Write each word in standard form. *(Lesson 2-3)*

1. seven thousand, six hundred fifteen _____

2. two thousand, eight hundred eleven _____

3. 3,000 + 70 + 9 _____   **4.** 5,000 + 200 + 60 + 4 _____

Write each missing value. *(Lesson 2-2)*

5. 6 tens = _____ ones   **6.** 9 hundreds = _____ tens

7. 8 tens = _____ ones   **8.** 4 hundreds = _____ tens

Mixed Review

9. Write the numbers six hundred nine
(2-1) and six hundred ninety.   _____ _____

10. In the number 689, which digit has the least value? Explain.
(2-1)

_____

11. Write which operation you would use. Then solve.
(1-5)

Lee Anne bought 6 oranges and 7 apples. How many pieces of fruit
did she buy?

_____

Use the bar graph to answer each question.

12. How much snow fell during December
(1-4) and January?

_____

13. How much snow fell in all four months?
(1-4)

_____

14. Which month had three times as much
(1-4) snow as November?

_____

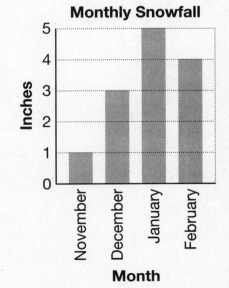

Monthly Snowfall

Daily Cumulative Review

Write the value of each underlined digit. *(Lesson 2-4)*

1. 13,5<u>6</u>7 _____   2. 46,<u>7</u>32 _____

3. 45<u>6</u>,326 _____

4. 906,04<u>1</u> _____

5. 9<u>7</u>5,135 _____

6. <u>1</u>01,010 _____

Complete the table. *(Lesson 2-3)*

	Number	100 More	100 Less
7.	7,856		
8.	2,419		
9.	5,299		
10.	4,701		

Mixed Review

Write the word name for each number.

11. 94 _____   12. 567 _____
(2-1)   (2-1)

13. 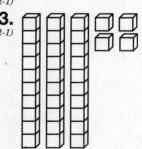   14.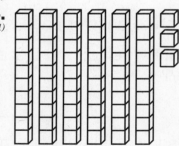
(2-1)   (2-1)

_____   _____

15. What are the next 3 numbers? 4, 8, 12, 16, _____, _____, _____
(1-11)

16. Greg is learning to play the tuba. He increases practice
(1-11) time by 4 minutes a day. Monday he practiced 9 minutes.
How many minutes will he practice on Friday?   _____

Name _____

Daily Cumulative Review

Make a list or use any strategy to help solve each problem. *(Lesson 2-5)*

1. Heather has 2 shirts and 3 skirts. How many different outfits can she make? _____

2. Suppose Thomas wanted to order 30 pairs of socks for his soccer team. He can buy socks in packs of 6 pairs or 1 pair.

   a. List all possible ways he could order 30 pairs of socks.

Packs of 6						
Packs of 1						

   b. How many ways are there to order 30 pairs of socks?

   _____

Write each number in standard form. *(Lesson 2-4)*

3. thirty-six thousand, five hundred eleven _____

4. eight hundred seventy-nine thousand, one hundred nine _____

5. 500,000 + 40,000 + 6,000 + 200 + 90 + 3 _____

6. 800,000 + 7,000 + 500 + 20 + 1 _____

Mixed Review

Complete the tables.

	Number	Number of Ones	Number of Tens	Number of Hundreds
7. (2-2)	200			2
8. (2-2)	400		40	
9. (2-2)	600	600		

	Number	100 More	100 Less
10. (2-3)	6,353		
11. (2-3)	1,504		
12. (2-3)	7,359		

© Scott Foresman Addison Wesley 3

Daily Cumulative Review

Compare. Use <, >, or =. *(Lesson 2-6)*

1. 59 ◯ 57

2. 213 ◯ 213

3. 69 ◯ 690

4. 871 ◯ 781

5. 3,232 ◯ 2,323

6. 721 ◯ 720

Make a list or use any strategy to help solve each problem. *(Lesson 2-5)*

7. Marcus needs $25 for a game he wants. How can he pay with the fewest ten and one dollar bills?

_____

8. Three girls are waiting in line to get a drink. Stacey is behind Janell. Tiana is first in line. In what order are the girls standing?

_____

9. Vernon and Suzanne had 14 orders for cookies in the last two days. If they had 6 orders yesterday, how many orders did they have today?

_____

Mixed Review

Use the bar graph to answer each question.

10. Which creature is the favorite of all?
(1-2)

_____

11. Which creatures had over 5 votes?
(1-2)

_____

12. How many students liked frogs or lizards?
(1-4)

_____

13. You are making a pictograph, and each of your symbols represents 2 students. How many symbols should there be for "Snake"?
(1-8)

_____

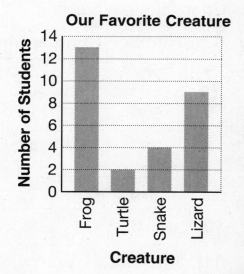

Our Favorite Creature

Daily Cumulative Review

Order from least to greatest. *(Lesson 2-7)*

1. 946, 964, 469 _____

2. 435, 534, 453 _____

3. 76, 706, 67 _____

4. 1,754, 1,645, 1,764 _____

Write "is less than," "is greater than," or "equals." *(Lesson 2-6)*

5. 45 _____ 54

6. 565 _____ 565

7. 2,999 _____ 2,990

8. 589 _____ 5,890

Mixed Review

Write each missing value.

9. 80 ones = _____ tens
(2-2)

10. _____ ones = 4 hundreds
(2-2)

11. 50 tens = _____ hundreds
(2-2)

12. _____ tens = 300 ones
(2-2)

Write the value of each underlined digit.

13. 853,621 _____
(2-4)

14. 999,999 _____
(2-4)

15. 303,030 _____
(2-4)

16. 123,456 _____
(2-4)

17. If the pattern continues, which shape should come next? _____
(1-11)

18. What are the next 3 numbers?
(1-11)

6, 12, 18, 24, _____, _____, _____

Daily Cumulative Review

Round to the nearest ten. *(Lesson 2-8)*

1. 45 _____

2. 13 _____

3. 67 _____

4. 222 _____

5. 387 _____

6. 789 _____

7. 91 _____

8. 559 _____

9. 101 _____

Order from greatest to least. *(Lesson 2-7)*

10. 509, 590, 500 _____

11. 4,590, 4,390, 3,490 _____

12. 6,061, 6,601, 6,106 _____

Mixed Review

13. To compare 6,843 and 6,861 you should look at the digits in the
(2-6)

_____ place

14. Using the digits 3, 9, and 6 only once, write the greatest and least
(2-4)   three-digit numbers you can.

_____

Write each number in standard form.

15. four hundred ninety-three _____
(2-1)

16. 900 + 90 + 9 _____
(2-1)

17. Complete the table. Write the rule.
(1-6)

In	26	21	14	19	7	23
Out	21	16	9			

Rule: _____

Name _____

Daily Cumulative Review

Round to the nearest hundred. *(Lesson 2-9)*

1. 789 _____

2. $567 _____

3. 329 _____

4. 899 _____

5. 241 _____

6. 611 _____

7. 150 _____

8. $462 _____

9. 938 _____

Round to the nearest ten. *(Lesson 2-8)*

10. 229 _____

11. 101 _____

12. 65 _____

13. 9 _____

14. 777 _____

15. 333 _____

16. 541 _____

17. 80 _____

18. 19 _____

Mixed Review

19. Circle the number that comes between 5,019 and 5,109.
(2-7)

    5,009   5,100   5,018   5,190

20. Circle the greatest number.
(2-7)

    3,716   3,617   3,176   3,761

Use the bar graph to answer each question.

21. How much more rain falls in the winter
(1-4) than in the fall?

_____

22. What is the total amount of rain that
(1-4) falls in spring and summer?

_____

23. What is the total amount of rain for
(1-4) the year?

_____

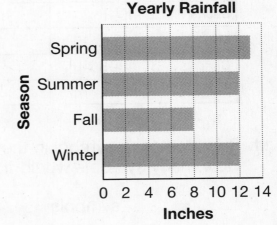

Yearly Rainfall

Daily Cumulative Review

Write each time two ways. *(Lesson 2-10)*

1.

2.

_____

_____

_____

_____

Round to the nearest hundred. *(Lesson 2-9)*

3. $765 _____

4. 123 _____

5. 899 _____

6. 313 _____

7. 549 _____

8. 250 _____

Mixed Review

Use the data to complete the table and the pictograph.

9.
(1-7)

Our Favorite Type of Movie

Type	Tally	Number
Science Fiction	⧫⧫⧫⧫ I	
Sports	⧫⧫⧫⧫ I	
Mystery	⧫⧫⧫⧫ III	
Cartoon	⧫⧫⧫⧫ ⧫⧫⧫⧫	
Comedy	⧫⧫⧫⧫ III	

10.
(1-8)

Our Favorite Type of Movie

Science Fiction	● ● ●
Sports	
Mystery	
Cartoon	
Comedy	

● = 2 students

11. Suppose each symbol in the pictograph above represents 3 students.
(1-8) How many symbols would there be for "Sports"?

_____ symbols

Name _____

Daily Cumulative Review

Write each time in two ways. *(Lesson 2-11)*

1.

_____

_____

2.

_____

_____

Write each time in two ways. *(Lesson 2-10)*

3.

_____

_____

4.

_____

_____

Mixed Review

Compare. Use <, >, or =.

5. 567 ◯ 576
(2-6)

6. 1,340 ◯ 134
(2-6)

7. 898 ◯ 898
(2-6)

Order from greatest to least.

8. 1,576; 1,756; 675 _____
(2-7)

9. 414; 4,114; 4,411 _____
(2-7)

10. Erin was born in 1978. Greg was born in 1980. Heather was born in
(2-7) 1973. Suzanne wants to put them in order from oldest to youngest.
Write the dates in order.

_____

Daily Cumulative Review

Write each time two ways. Write A.M. or P.M. *(Lesson 2-12)*

1.

art
class

_____

_____

2.

piano
lesson

_____

_____

Write each time two ways. *(Lesson 2-11)*

3.

_____

_____

4.

_____

_____

Mixed Review

5. How many minutes are between 9:40 and 9:55? _____
(2-10)

6. Suppose it's 3:15. What time will it be 15 minutes later? _____
(2-10)

Write each number in standard form.

7. three thousand, twenty-seven _____
(2-3)

8. nine thousand, four hundred one _____
(2-3)

9. one thousand, one _____
(2-3)

10. seven thousand, seven hundred seventy-seven _____
(2-3)

11. four thousand, forty _____
(2-3)

Daily Cumulative Review

Solve each problem. *(Lesson 2-13)*

1. Jillian's basketball practice lasts for 1 hour and 15 minutes. If it begins at 4:00 P.M., what time will it end?

_____

2. Mark's favorite cartoon starts at 8:30 A.M. It is now 7:50 A.M. How much time does Mark have to wait until it starts?

_____

3. Suppose it is 9:40 P.M. What time will it be in half an hour?

_____

Solve each problem. *(Lesson 2-12)*

4. Write a time that is between midnight and half past twelve at night.

_____

5. Write a time that is between 3:30 P.M. and a quarter to four P.M.

_____

6. When it is a quarter past five, what number is the minute hand pointing to?

_____

Mixed Review

7. Name 3 two-digit numbers that round to 50 when rounded to the nearest ten.
(2-8)

_____

8. Name 3 three-digit numbers that round to 370 when rounded to the nearest ten.
(2-8)

_____

_____

9. Michael needs $45 for a coat. How can he pay with the least ten a one dollar bills?
(2-5)

_____

Daily Cumulative Review

Use the calendar to answer 1–3. *(Lesson 2-14)*

July						
Sun	Mon	Tue	Wed	Thu	Fri	Sat
			1	2	3	4
5	6	7	8	9	10	11
12	13	14	15	16	17	18
19	20	21	22	23	24	25
26	27	28	29	30	31	

1. How many Fridays are in this month? _____

2. What day of the week is July 14th? _____

3. What is the date of the fourth Thursday in July? _____

Solve each problem. *(Lesson 2-13)*

Brian, Tammy, and Mary had practice at 5:30 P.M. Each practiced for the amount of time shown. When did each child finish their practice?

	Child	Practice Time	Finish Time
4.	Brian	55 minutes	_____
5.	Tammy	1 hour and 10 minutes	_____
6.	Mary	1 hour and 25 minutes	_____

Mixed Review

7. 12, 15, 18, 21
(1-11)

a. What is the difference between each pair of numbers ? _____

b. What is the pattern? _____

c. What are the next 3 numbers? _____, _____, _____

Daily Cumulative Review

Write each amount of time. *(Lesson 2-15)*

1. Figure how much time is needed for each activity on this list and write it down.

Activity	Total Time
a. The bus ride home begins at 3:30 P.M. and lasts until 3:55 P.M.	_____
b. You have baseball practice from 4:15 P.M. until 5:30 P.M.	_____
c. Your best friend comes over at 3:45 P.M. and leaves at 5:30 P.M.	_____

Answer each question. *(Lesson 2-14)*

2. What is the month after August? _____

3. Name the 11th month. _____

4. Which month comes before March? _____

Mixed Review

Use the pictograph to answer each question.

5. How many students have birthdays in June?
   (1-1)

   _____

6. Which month has the most birthdays?
   (1-1)

   _____

7. How many birthdays are in July and August?
   (1-4)

   _____

8. Which month has the fewest birthdays?
   (1-1)

   _____

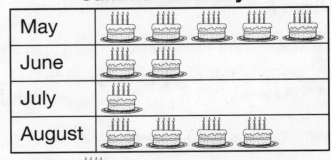

Summer Birthdays

May	🎂 🎂 🎂 🎂 🎂
June	🎂 🎂
July	🎂
August	🎂 🎂 🎂 🎂

Each 🎂 equals 2 birthdays.

Daily Cumulative Review

Use basic facts and place value to complete each problem. *(Lesson 3-1)*

1. 2 + 5 = _____

    20 + _____ = 70

    _____ + 500 = 700

2. 5 + 7 = _____

    _____ + 70 = 120

    500 + _____ = 1,200

3. 4 + _____ = 11

    _____ + 70 = 110

    400 + 700 = _____

4. _____ + 3 = 9

    60 + _____ = 90

    _____ + 300 = 900

5. 8 + 5 = _____

    80 + _____ = 130

    _____ + 500 = 1,300

6. 4 + _____ = 8

    _____ + 40 = 80

    _____ + 400 = 800

Estimate how long it would take you to do each. *(Lesson 2-15)*

7. take a shower   _____

8. eat lunch   _____

9. read 20 pages   _____

10. wash the dishes   _____

Mixed Review

11. If it is 7:51 now, in how many minutes will it be 8:00? _____
(2-11)

12. What is the smallest number that rounds to 800
(2-9) when you round to the nearest hundred? _____

Write "is less than," "is greater than," or "equals."

13. 6,789 _____ 6,789
(2-6)

14. 5,643 _____ 6,543
(2-6)

15. 331 _____ 329
(2-6)

Daily Cumulative Review

Find each sum. You may use the hundred chart to help.
(Lesson 3-2)

1	2	3	4	5	6	7	8	9	10
11	12	13	14	15	16	17	18	19	20
21	22	23	24	25	26	27	28	29	30
31	32	33	34	35	36	37	38	39	40
41	42	43	44	45	46	47	48	49	50
51	52	53	54	55	56	57	58	59	60
61	62	63	64	65	66	67	68	69	70
71	72	73	74	75	76	77	78	79	80
81	82	83	84	85	86	87	88	89	90
91	92	93	94	95	96	97	98	99	100

1. 64 + 29 = _____

2. 33 + 30 = _____

3. $43 + $39 = _____

4. 30 + 35 = _____

5. 27 + 19 = _____

6. 9 + 47 = _____

7. $67 + $18 = _____

Find each sum using mental math. *(Lesson 3-1)*

8. $30 + 60 = _____

9. 500 + 300 = _____

10. 70 + 80 = _____

11. $400 + $600 = _____

Mixed Review

Order from least to greatest.

12. 409; 399; 425 _____
(2-7)

13. 2,641; 2,589; 257 _____
(2-7)

14. 7,077; 7,777; 7,007 _____
(2-7)

15. Write a number sentence and use it to solve the problem.
(1-5)

Katy read 9 books. 4 were fiction. The rest were nonfiction.
How many were nonfiction?

_____

16. What is the greatest number that rounds to 800
(2-9) when you round to the nearest hundred? _____

Daily Cumulative Review

**Find each missing number. You may use color cubes
to help.** *(Lesson 3-3)*

1. _____ + 6 = 25   **2.** _____ + 7 = 21

3. 9 + _____ = 24   **4.** 8 + _____ = 22

5. _____ + 3 = 18   **6.** 2 + _____ = 19

Find each sum. You may use the hundred chart to help.
(Lesson 3-2)

7. 65 + 23 = _____

8. 15 + 59 = _____

9. 51 + 16 = _____

10. 25 + 45 = _____

11. $77 + $14 = _____

12. 39 + 19 = _____

13. 22 + 44 = _____

1	2	3	4	5	6	7	8	9	10
11	12	13	14	15	16	17	18	19	20
21	22	23	24	25	26	27	28	29	30
31	32	33	34	35	36	37	38	39	40
41	42	43	44	45	46	47	48	49	50
51	52	53	54	55	56	57	58	59	60
61	62	63	64	65	66	67	68	69	70
71	72	73	74	75	76	77	78	79	80
81	82	83	84	85	86	87	88	89	90
91	92	93	94	95	96	97	98	99	100

Mixed Review

Use the calendar to answer each question.

14. How many Saturdays
(2-14) are in this month?

_____

15. What day of the week
(2-14) is the 27th?

_____

November						
Sun	Mon	Tue	Wed	Thu	Fri	Sat
1	2	3	4	5	6	7
8	9	10	11	12	13	14
15	16	17	18	19	20	21
22	23	24	25	26	27	28
29	30					

16. Write the value of each digit in 683,741.
(2-4)

    a. 8 _____   **b.** 3 _____

    c. 7 _____   **d.** 1 _____

    e. 6 _____   **f.** 4 _____

Name _____

Daily Cumulative Review

Estimate each sum. *(Lesson 3-4)*

1. 59 + 21 _____ **2.** 813 + 188 _____

3. $42 + $29 _____ **4.** 444 + 123 _____

5. $189 + $239 _____ **6.** 71 + 16 _____

Use patterns to find each missing number. *(Lesson 3-3)*

7. _____ + 8 = 14 **8.** 5 + _____ = 14 **9.** _____ + 10 = 14

10. _____ + 9 = 18 **11.** 8 + _____ = 18 **12.** _____ + 11 = 18

Mixed Review

Write each time two ways.

13.
(2-10)

Possible answers:

_____

_____

14.
(2-11)

Possible answers:

_____

_____

15. Round 89 to the nearest hundred. _____
(2-9)

Write the word name for each number.

16. 2,511 _____
(2-3)

17. 7,888 _____
(2-3)

18. What are the next 3 numbers?
(1-11)

40, 50, 60, _____, _____, _____

Daily Cumulative Review

Find each sum. You may use place-value blocks to help.
(Lesson 3-5)

1. 14 + 38

    a. How many ones? _____

    b. Do you need to regroup? _____

    c. How many tens? _____

    d. Do you need to regroup? _____

    e. 14 + 38 = _____

2. 66 + 35 = _____   **3.** 39 + 99 = _____

4. 26 + 76 = _____   **5.** 45 + 79 = _____

Estimate each sum. *(Lesson 3-4)*

6. 27 + 89 _____   **7.** $775 + $301 _____

8. 932 + 451 _____   **9.** 94 + 56 _____

10. 36 + 63 _____   **11.** $111 + $270 _____

Mixed Review

12. Figure out how much time is needed for each activity on this list and
₍₂₋₁₅₎ write it down.

Activity	Total Time
a. Art class begins at 1:45 P.M. and lasts until 2:30 P.M.	_____
b. Practice begins at 4:15 P.M. and ends at 5:00 P.M.	_____

13. Name the eighth month. _____
₍₂₋₁₄₎

14. What month comes before June? _____
₍₂₋₁₄₎

Name _____

Daily Cumulative Review

Add. Estimate to check. *(Lesson 3-6)*

1.   7 8
     + 2 2

2.   7 7
     + 2 4

3.   1 9
     + 6 5

4. $9 6
     + 8

Find each sum. You may use place-value blocks to help. *(Lesson 3-5)*

5. $39 + 76 =$ _____

6. $75 + 47 =$ _____

7. $18 + 84 =$ _____

8. $33 + 49 =$ _____

Mixed Review

9. Estimate the sum of $59 and $49. _____
(3-4)

10. Write a number sentence and use it to solve the problem.
(1-5)

Kerri had 9 fish. She bought 7 more. How many fish did she have then?

_____

Use the pictograph to answer each question.

11. How many girls like snakes?
(1-1)

_____

12. How many more boys than girls like snakes?
(1-4)

_____

13. Suppose each symbol in the pictograph represented 3 students. How many symbols would there be for girls?
(1-8)

_____

Like Snakes

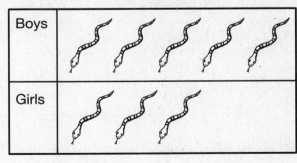

Each 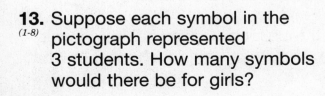 is equal to 4 students.

Daily Cumulative Review

Add. Estimate to check. *(Lesson 3-7)*

1. $754
   + 289

2. 696
   + 217

3. 571
   + 89

4. 488
   + 699

Add. Estimate to check. *(Lesson 3-6)*

5. 77
   + 88

6. $69
   + 94

7. 26
   + 85

8. 98
   + 9

Mixed Review

9. Write a number between 3,589 and 4,089.
(2-7)

_____

Write each number in standard form.

10. nine hundred sixty-one thousand, thirty-two _____
(2-4)

11. eighty-four thousand, one hundred ten _____
(2-4)

12. two thousand, three hundred fourteen _____
(2-4)

Complete the table.

	Number	100 More	100 Less
13. (2-3)	9,756		
14. (2-3)	3,390		
15. (2-3)	6,109		

16. Four boys were standing in line at the balloon pop game. Kevin was
(2-5) third in line. Don was behind Kevin. Tony was behind Charles. In what
    order are the boys standing?

_____

Name _____

Daily Cumulative Review

Add. *(Lesson 3-8)*

1.   4,800
     + 3,700

2. $6,823
     + 1,345

3.   5,355
     + 2,691

4.   3,379
     +   923

Add. Estimate to check. *(Lesson 3-7)*

5. $365
     + 271

6.   488
     + 98

7.   821
     + 255

8. $291
     + 659

Mixed Review

9. I am a 2-digit number. If you add me to 7 you will get a sum of 39.
(3-3) What number am I?

_____

10. Round to find which two numbers have a sum of about 800.
(3-4)

512   455   368   608   224

_____

11. Annette wants to let her dog run for 30 minutes. If she starts at
(2-13) 9:15 A.M., what time should she call the dog in?

_____

12. Suppose you waited 18 minutes for your practice to start. About how
(2-11) many minutes did you wait? Round to the nearest ten minutes.

_____

13. Circle the number that comes between 4,709 and 4,907.
(2-7)

4,708   4,908   4,909   4,904

14. Circle the number that comes between 7,317 and 7,567.
(2-7)

7,300   7,618   7,425   7,690

Name _____

Daily Cumulative Review

Add. *(Lesson 3-9)*

1.	5 6	2.	5 2 8	3.	8 8 0	4.	3 7 1
	8 7		1 4 5		3 1 5		9
	+ 6		+ 7 3		+ 4 0 9		+ 2 6 9

Add. *(Lesson 3-8)*

5.	5,731	6.	7,100	7.	$3,379	8.	2,788
	+ 3,658		+ 2,700		+ 2,155		+ 5,093

9.	6,314	10.	1,472	11.	2,745	12.	7,141
	+ 2,123		+ 2,448		+ 5,781		+ 2,298

Mixed Review

Write each number in standard form.

13. forty-four thousand, eight hundred three _____
(2-4)

14. six hundred sixty-seven thousand _____
(2-4)

15. twenty-one thousand, five hundred eleven _____
(2-4)

16. Complete the table. Write the rule.
(1-6)

In	8	13	15	17	22	16
Out	10		17		24	

Rule: _____

17. What's another way to write 5 minutes before six? _____
(2-10)

18. Estimate the sum of $78 and $31. _____
(3-4)

Daily Cumulative Review

Use any strategy to solve. *(Lesson 3-10)*

1. The Bears beat the Panthers in a softball game. The scores were 4 runs apart and there were 20 runs scored in the game. How many runs did each team score?

   _____

2. The Bears lost to the Cheetahs by 6 runs. There were 24 runs scored in the game. How many runs did the Cheetahs score?

   _____

3. The sum of two numbers is 54. The numbers are 8 apart. What are they?

   _____

4. The sum of the two numbers is 32. The numbers are 16 apart. What are they?

   _____

Add. *(Lesson 3-9)*

5.
```
  340
   79
+   9
```

6.
```
   67
  691
+ 520
```

7.
```
  537
   55
+ 270
```

8.
```
  726
  765
+ 116
```

Mixed Review

Round to the nearest hundred.

9. $567 _____   **10.** 845 _____
(2-9)   *(2-9)*

11. 303 _____   **12.** $249 _____
(2-9)   *(2-9)*

13. If it is 5:50, in how many minutes will it be 6:00? _____
(2-11)

14. Niles puts muffins in the oven at 3:00 P.M. They should cook for 25 minutes. What time should he take them out?
(2-13)

_____

Daily Cumulative Review

Use mental math to find each sum. *(Lesson 3-11)*

1. 41 + 78 = _____

2. 29 + 40 = _____

3. 33 + 72 = _____

4. 35 + 45 = _____

5. 29 + 4 = _____

6. 99 + 7 = _____

Use any strategy to solve. *(Lesson 3-10)*

7. The sum of two numbers is 90. The numbers are 6 apart. What are they?

_____

8. The sum of two numbers is 85. The numbers are 17 apart. What are they?

_____

9. The Blues beat the Reds by 3 runs. There were 15 runs scored in the game. How many runs did the Blues score?

_____

Mixed Review

Use the line graph to answer each question.

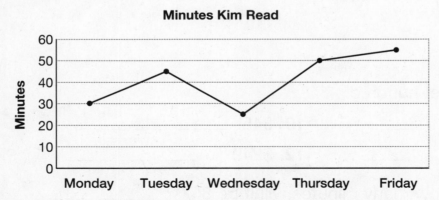

Minutes Kim Read

10. How many minutes did Kim read on Tuesday? _____
(1-3)

11. What day did she read 50 minutes? _____
(1-3)

12. Which day did Kim read the most? _____
(1-3)

Daily Cumulative Review

Write the total value in cents. *(Lesson 3-12)*

1.

_____

2.

_____

3.

_____

4.

_____

Use mental math to find each sum. *(Lesson 3-11)*

5. 57 + 39 = _____   **6.** 27 + 63 = _____

7. 71 + 9 = _____   **8.** 35 + 60 = _____

Mixed Review

Add. Estimate to check.

9.
(3-7)
```
  6 2 6
+   2 7
```

10.
(3-7)
```
  6 0 4
+ 4 2 8
```

11.
(3-7)
```
  1 3 3
+ 8 7 5
```

12.
(3-7)
```
$9 7 5
+   9 9
```

Find each sum using mental math.

13. There are 40 students on one tour and 50 students
(3-1) on another tour. How many students are there altogether? _____

14. A new dress costs $30. A new pair of shoes costs $20.
(3-1) How much would it cost to buy the dress and shoes? _____

Name _____

Daily Cumulative Review

Write the total value in dollars and cents. *(Lesson 3-13)*

1.

2.

_____   _____

Write the total value in cents. *(Lesson 3-12)*

3.

4.

_____   _____

Mixed Review

5. Find the sum of
(3-8) 4,239 and 1,685. _____

6. Find the sum of
(3-8) 4,700 and 5,000. _____

Complete.

7. 7 + 7 = _____
(3-1)

70 + _____ = 140

_____ + 700 = 1,400

8. $8 + $_____ = $12
(3-1)

$_____ + $40 = $120

$800 + $400 = $_____

9. Complete the table. Write the rule.
(1-6)

In	3	7	9	15	23	30
Out	12	16	18			

Rule: _____

Daily Cumulative Review

**List which coins and bills you would use to make change.
Then write the change in dollars and cents.** *(Lesson 3-14)*

1. Corky buys a drink that costs $0.55. He pays with $1.00

_____

2. Mike buys a candy bar that costs $0.60. He pays with $1.00

_____

3. Beth buys $3.89 worth of cookies. She pays with $5.00

_____

Write the total value in dollars and cents. *(Lesson 3-13)*

4.

5.

_____   _____

Mixed Review

6. Add 76 and 19. _____
(3-6)

7. Write two addends with a sum of 348. _____
(3-7)

8. I am a 2-digit number. If you add me to 7 you will
(3-3) get a sum of 43. What number am I?   _____

9. What basic fact can you use to find 400 + 700? _____
(3-1)

Name _____

Daily Cumulative Review

Add. Estimate to check. *(Lesson 3-15)*

1. $6 . 7 8
    + 3 . 1 7

2. $5 . 8 9
    + 4 . 6 7

3. $0 . 7 4
    + 7 . 5 6

4. $4 . 4 4
    + 3 . 6 0

List which coins and bills you would use to make change.
Then write the change in dollars and cents. *(Lesson 3-14)*

5. Jeff buys a coloring book that costs $1.79. He pays with $2.00.

   _____

6. Angie buys a pack of tennis balls that costs $3.68.
   She pays with $5.00.

   _____

Mixed Review

7. Write a time that is between noon and a quarter past twelve in
   (2-12) the afternoon.

   _____

8. Jaci's practice is at 5:15. She arrived at 5:18. Is she early or late?
   (2-11)

   _____

9. What is the greatest number that rounds to 500 when rounded to the
   (2-9) nearest hundred?

   _____

10. Circle the number that comes between 2,020 and 2,202.
    (2-7)

    2,222   2,022   2,010   2,002

11. Marcus needs $35 for a computer game. How can he pay with the
    (2-5) least ten and one dollar bills?

    _____

Daily Cumulative Review

Use front-end estimation to estimate each sum.
(Lesson 3-16)

1. $5.13
   + 2.28

2.   828
   + 520

3.   751
     133
   + 202

4. $4.33
     2.87
   + 5.16

Add. Estimate to check. *(Lesson 3-15)*

5. $4.78
   + 5.13

6. $1.06
   + 3.99

7. $8.60
   + 3.45

8. $7.32
   + 0.74

Mixed Review

Use the bar graph to answer each question.

9. Which 2 nuts combined had the
   (1-4) same amount of votes as pecans?

   _____

10. Which nut had twice as many
    (1-4) votes as almonds?

    _____

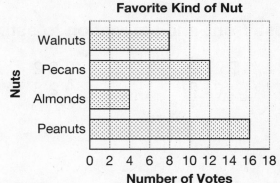

Favorite Kind of Nut

Use the pictograph to answer each question.

11. Do more children or adults
    (1-4) like apples?

    _____

12. How many children like apples?
    (1-4)

    _____

13. How many children and adults
    (1-4) like apples?

    _____

Like Apples

| Children | 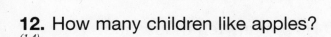 |
| Adults | |

Each is equal to 3 people.

Daily Cumulative Review

Write if you need an exact answer or an estimate. Then solve. *(Lesson 3-17)*

Food	
Milk	$2.15
Bread	$1.23
Cereal	$2.98
Juice	$3.47
Chips	$2.57
Soda	$1.08
Ice Cream	$2.64

1. Juan has a $5 bill. Does he have enough money to buy soda and chips? Explain.

_____

2. How much would it cost to buy milk, cereal, and juice?

_____

3. Mrs. Miller began shopping at 10:45 A.M. When she finished it was 11:50 A.M. How long did she spend shopping.

_____

Use front-end estimation to estimate each sum. *(Lesson 3-16)*

4. $5.7 7
   + 3.1 2

5.   2 8 2
   + 9 2 8

6. $5.5 5
    3.8 7
   + 4.2 3

7.   1 7 8
     4 5 0
   + 6 2 2

Mixed Review

8. Do you need to regroup 10 tens for 1 hundred when you add 567 + 451?
(3-7)

_____

9. How many thousands is 300,000? How many ten thousands?
(2-4)

_____

Estimate each sum.

10. 487 + 297 _____
(3-4)

11. $808 + $278 _____
(3-4)

Daily Cumulative Review

Write a number sentence for each. Then solve. *(Lesson 4-1)*

1. Tara has finished 5 problems on her math page. The page has 12 problems. How many problems does she have left to do?

   _____

2. Zack has $5. He buys a book for $3. How much money does he have left?

   _____

3. Paul invites nine friends to his pool party. Two people cannot come. How many people are there for the party?

   _____

Write if you need an exact answer or an estimate. Then solve. *(Lesson 3-17)*

4. Robin wants to buy three stuffed animals that cost $4.25, $3.95, and $4.95. Will $10 be enough money? Explain.

   _____

   _____

5. Each drink costs $0.65. How much would it cost to buy 3 drinks?

   _____

Mixed Review

Write the value of each underlined digit.

6. 4<u>5</u>,098 _____   7. <u>6</u>47,405 _____
   (2-4)   (2-4)

Find each sum using mental math.

8. 800 + 300 = _____   9. $40 + 90 = _____
   (3-1)   (3-1)

Daily Cumulative Review

Complete. *(Lesson 4-2)*

1. 5 − 2 = _____

50 − _____ = 30

_____ − 200 = 300

2. 15 − 7 = _____

_____ − 70 = 80

1,500 − _____ = 800

3. 14 − _____ = 11

_____ − 30 = 110

1,400 − 300 = _____

4. $_____ − $4 = $14

$180 − $_____ = $140

$_____ − $400 = $1,400

Write a number sentence for each. Then solve. *(Lesson 4-1)*

5. A box of cookies contained eighteen cookies. Now there are only eight. How many cookies were taken?

_____

6. Five squirrels are playing in a tree. Three run away. How many are in the tree now?

_____

Mixed Review

7. Talia's purchases total $4.56. She pays with $5.00. Write
(3-14) three ways you could make change.

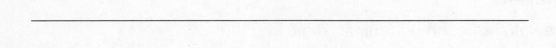

_____

_____

_____

Use mental math to find each sum.

8. 61 + 9 = _____
(3-11)

9. 7 + 33 = _____
(3-11)

10. 37 + 49 = _____
(3-11)

11. 52 + 18 = _____
(3-11)

Name _____

Daily Cumulative Review

Find each difference. You may use a hundred chart to help. *(Lesson 4-3)*

1. 44 − 27 = _____

2. 39 − 22 = _____

3. 79 − 26 = _____

4. $66 − $54 = _____

Find each difference using mental math. *(Lesson 4-2)*

5. 80 − 30 = _____

6. $100 − $70 = _____

7. $1,400 − $300 = _____

8. 1,900 − 1,400 = _____

Mixed Review

9. Is the sum of $4.67 + $6.23 + $8.44 greater than $15.00? Explain.
(3-16)

_____

_____

10. Find the sum of
(3-8) 1,200 and 6,000.

11. Find the sum of 734 and 3,118.
(3-8)

_____   _____

12. In 2 minutes, it will be 3:00. What time is it now? _____
(2-11)

Write each number in standard form.

13. nine thousand five _____
(2-3)

14. 6,000 + 800 + 30 _____
(2-3)

15. Cheri said, "I lost a coin! I had $7.86. Now I only have
(3-13) 1 five-dollar bill, 2 one-dollar bills, 3 quarters, and one
penny." What coin did Cheri lose?

_____

16. The Mustangs beat the Wildcats by 4 runs. There were
(3-10) 18 runs scored. How many runs did the Mustangs score?

_____

Daily Cumulative Review

Estimate each difference. *(Lesson 4-4)*

1. 62 − 47 _____

2. $7.75 − $3.99 _____

3. 389 − 222 _____

4. 471 − 301 _____

Use mental math to find each difference. *(Lesson 4-3)*

5. 50 − 20 = _____

6. $80 − $30 = _____

7. 90 − 40 = _____

8. 60 − 40 = _____

Mixed Review

Find each sum.

9.
(3-9)
$$\begin{array}{r} 656 \\ 137 \\ +\ 82 \\ \hline \end{array}$$

10.
(3-9)
$$\begin{array}{r} 511 \\ 218 \\ +\ 291 \\ \hline \end{array}$$

11.
(3-15)
$$\begin{array}{r} \$3.55 \\ +\ 2.50 \\ \hline \end{array}$$

12.
(3-15)
$$\begin{array}{r} \$6.79 \\ +\ 9.43 \\ \hline \end{array}$$

13. Suppose it is 5:40 A.M. What time will it be in 20 minutes?
(2-13)

_____

14. If it is 1:23, in how many minutes will it be 1:30?
(2-11)

_____

15. Complete the table. Write the rule.
(1-6)

In	17	21	27	18	30	12
Out	11	15	21			

Rule: _____

16. Jennifer has a five-dollar bill, 3 one-dollar bills, 2 quarters,
(3-13) 3 dimes, 1 nickel, and 4 pennies. How much money does she have?

_____

Daily Cumulative Review

Regroup 1 ten for 10 ones. You may use place-value blocks or draw a picture to help. *(Lesson 4-5)*

1. 47 = 3 tens, _____ ones

2. 94 = 8 tens, _____ ones

3. 38 = _____ tens, 18 ones

4. 70 = _____ tens, 10 ones

5. _____ = 5 tens, 17 ones

6. _____ = 6 tens, 14 ones

Estimate each difference. *(Lesson 4-4)*

7. 48 − 22 _____

8. 52 − 19 _____

9. $8.99 − $2.67 _____

10. 590 − 160 _____

Mixed Review

11. If the pattern continues, which shape
(1-11) should come next? _____

12. In the number 159, which digit has the greatest value? Explain.
(2-1)

_____

13. Using the digits 1, 9, and 5, write a number with a 9 in
(2-4) the hundred thousands place and a 1 in the thousands place.

_____

14. Write any 4 numbers less than 600 that round to 600
(2-9) when you round to the nearest hundred.

_____

15. Tania wants to buy three books for $1.75, $2.95, and $4.55.
(3-15) Will $10.00 be enough? Explain.

_____

Name _____

Daily Cumulative Review

Find each difference. You may use place-value blocks or draw a picture to help. *(Lesson 4-6)*

1. 52 − 7 = _____

2. 38 − 19 = _____

3. $67 − $28 = _____

4. 23 − 15 = _____

Regroup 1 hundred for 10 tens. You may use place-value blocks or draw a picture to help. *(Lesson 4-5)*

5. 872 = 7 hundreds, _____ tens, 2 ones

6. 403 = 3 hundreds, _____ tens, 3 ones

7. 514 = 4 hundreds, _____ tens, 4 ones

8. 777 = 6 hundreds, _____ tens, 7 ones

9. 686 = 5 hundreds, _____ tens, 6 ones

Mixed Review

Find each sum.

10. $4,754 + $5,219 = _____
(3-8)

11. 76 + 541 + 279 = _____
(3-9)

12. Continue the pattern. Then write the rule.
(4-2)

In	30	40	50	60	70	80
Out	50	60	70			

Rule: _____

13. The sum of two numbers is 82. The numbers are 10 apart.
(3-10) What are they?

_____

14. Jason ate lunch at 12:30 P.M. and went swimming 3 hours and 30
(2-13) minutes later. What time did he go swimming?

_____

Daily Cumulative Review

Subtract. Check each answer. *(Lesson 4-7)*

1. 5 6 − 2 7	**2.** 6 7 − 2 3	**3.** $9 1 − 3 6	**4.** 9 2 − 9
5. 2 2 − 1 6	**6.** 7 0 − 4 8	**7.** $6 5 − 3 9	**8.** 5 0 − 3 1

Find each difference. You may use place-value blocks or draw a picture to help. *(Lesson 4-6)*

9. Rhomi has read 16 pages of his 61-page book. How many more pages does he have left to read? _____

10. Gena has 55 problems to do for homework. She has done 36 problems. How many more problems does she have to do? _____

11. Your class needs to read 60 books to win the contest. So far the class has read 24 books. How many more books need to be read? _____

12. David needs 50 proofs of purchase to receive a free basketball from a cereal company. So far, he has 28 proofs of purchase. How many more does he need? _____

Mixed Review

Write the next four numbers.

13. 90, 80, 70, 60, _____, _____, _____, _____
(1-11)

14. 33, 30, 27, 24, _____, _____, _____, _____
(1-11)

15. Mica's swimming class lasts for 55 minutes.
(2-13) If it begins at 4:05 P.M., what time will it end? _____

Daily Cumulative Review

Find each difference. You may use place-value blocks or draw a picture to help. *(Lesson 4-8)*

1. 318 − 64 = _____   **2.** 454 − 272 = _____

3. 181 − 53 = _____   **4.** 588 − 374 = _____

Subtract. Check each answer. *(Lesson 4-7)*

5. 7 2
     −   9

6.   7 0
     − 2 1

7.   8 7
     − 5 9

8. $3 1
     − 1 3

Mixed Review

9. Estimate the sum of 815 and 167. _____
(3-4)

Order from least to greatest.

10. 755; 725; 630; 635 _____
(2-7)

11. 3,689; 4,976; 3,896; 4,697 _____
(2-7)

12. How many minutes are between 12:40 and 12:55? _____
(2-10)

13. Which digit has the least value in 14,789? Explain.
(2-4)

_____

_____

14. Jamie has a blue shirt and a green shirt, black pants and
(2-5) tan pants. How many different outfits can he make?

_____

15. The sum of two numbers is 31. The numbers are
(3-10) 7 apart. What are they?

_____

Name _____

Daily Cumulative Review

Subtract. Check each answer. *(Lesson 4-9)*

1.
   5 1 4
   − 2 3 3

2.
   $343
   − 3 3 6

3.
   3 6 8
   −   8 6

4.
   6 2 2
   − 4 4 2

Find each difference. You may use place-value blocks or draw a picture to help. *(Lesson 4-8)*

5. 366 − 296 = _____

6. 236 − 83 = _____

7. 549 − 231 = _____

8. 300 − 40 = _____

9. 478 − 136 = _____

10. 587 − 318 = _____

Mixed Review

Estimate each difference.

11. $6.21 − $3.76 = _____
(4-4)

12. 67 − 31 = _____
(4-4)

13. Use the fewest coins to make 48 cents.
(3-12)

_____

14. What is the sum of 33, 552, and 119? _____
(3-9)

Round each number to the nearest ten.

15. 621 _____
(2-8)

16. 788 _____
(2-8)

17. 345 _____
(2-8)

18. 572 _____
(2-8)

19. 248 _____
(2-8)

20. 191 _____
(2-8)

Write each missing value.

21. 50 ones = _____ tens
(2-2)

22. _____ ones = 6 hundreds
(2-2)

23. 90 tens = _____ hundreds
(2-2)

24. _____ tens = 800 ones
(2-2)

25. To compare 6,783 and 6,738 you
(2-6)

should look at the digits in the _____ place.

Daily Cumulative Review

Subtract. Check each answer. *(Lesson 4-10)*

1.
```
   6 5 1
 - 1 7 6
```

2.
```
   3 4 5
 - 2 9 6
```

3.
```
  $9 7 2
 - 2 9 3
```

4.
```
   4 2 0
 - 3 7 5
```

Subtract. Check each answer. *(Lesson 4-9)*

5.
```
  $6 5 6
 - 2 7 5
```

6.
```
   3 4 8
 - 1 2 9
```

7.
```
   7 4 2
 - 5 5 0
```

8.
```
   5 5 5
 - 3 2 9
```

Mixed Review

Use the calendar to answer each question.

9. How many Sundays are
(2-14) in the month shown?

_____

10. What day of the week
(2-14) is the 28th?

_____

September						
Sun	Mon	Tue	Wed	Thu	Fri	Sat
		1	2	3	4	5
6	7	8	9	10	11	12
13	14	15	16	17	18	19
20	21	22	23	24	25	26
27	28	29	30			

11. Mary's school starts at 8:45 A.M. She arrives at 8:27 A.M.
(2-11) Is she early or late?

_____

12. Estimate to decide which sum is greater than 1,000:
(3-7) 685 + 423 or 211 + 733.

_____

13. Find the sum of $6.78 + $2.98. _____
(3-15)

14. What basic fact could you use to find 1,500 − 800?
(4-2)

_____

Name _____

Daily Cumulative Review

Subtract. Check each answer. *(Lesson 4-11)*

1.	2.	3.	4.
406 − 192	708 − 169	303 − 159	107 − 28

5.	6.	7.	8.
600 − 389	$500 − 56	400 − 265	300 − 197

Subtract. Check each answer. *(Lesson 4-10)*

9.	10.	11.	12.
311 − 176	730 − 562	$586 − 397	322 − 135

Mixed Review

Use the pictograph to answer each question.

13. How many students does
$^{(1-4)}$ each symbol represent?

_____

14. How many boys have dogs?
$_{(1-4)}$

_____

15. How many more boys
$^{(1-4)}$ than girls have dogs?

_____

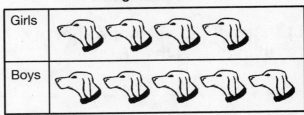

Dogs Owned

| Girls | |
| Boys | |

Each  is equal to 5 students.

Round each number to the nearest hundred.

16. $567 _____   **17.** 812 _____   **18.** 98 _____
$_{(2-9)}$ $_{(2-9)}$ $_{(2-9)}$

19. Write two addends with a sum of 316.
$_{(3-7)}$

_____

Daily Cumulative Review

Solve. Check each answer. *(Lesson 4-12)*

1. $7,8 0 0
    −   9 9 5

2. 8,2 0 0
    − 5,8 0 0

3. 5,6 7 8
    − 4,7 6 9

4. 4,4 6 2
    − 2,8 5 6

Subtract. Check each answer. *(Lesson 4-11)*

5. 7 0 5
    − 2 1 1

6. 9 0 0
    −   5 9

7. 3 0 7
    − 1 9 6

8. $2 0 7
    − 1 3 8

Mixed Review

9. *(4-6)* Suppose you had a quarter, 1 dime, and 3 nickels. If you lose 2 of your nickels, how much money would you have?

_____

10. *(3-8)* Estimate to see if the sum of 7,891 and 3,720 is greater than or less than 10,000.

_____

11. *(3-8)* Estimate to see if the sum of 4,732 and 2,298 is greater than or less than 8,000.

_____

12. *(2-13)* "This movie lasts for 1 hour and 49 minutes," says Kathy. If it begins at 8:00 P.M., what time will the movie end?

_____

13. *(2-8)* Name 4 two-digit numbers that round to 30 when rounded to the nearest ten.

_____

14. *(4-8)* Suppose you had 137 marbles and your brother had 241. How many more does your brother have?

_____

Daily Cumulative Review

Solve each problem. *(Lesson 4-13)*

1. Mr. and Mrs. Sisco want to take their 2 children to the zoo. Their children are 7 and 10 years old.

   a. How much will it cost for the family to go to the zoo on a Wednesday?

   _____

   b. How much more will it cost for the family to go to the zoo on a Saturday?

   _____

Zoo Admission Prices	
Monday through Friday	
Children under 12	$3
Adults	$5
Saturday and Sunday	
Children under 12	$4
Adults	$6

2. How much would it cost for 2 adults and 1 child that is 9 years old to go to the zoo on Sunday?

   _____

Solve. Check each answer. *(Lesson 4-12)*

3.	4.	5.	6.
$4,278$	$\$4,780$	$1,579$	$4,799$
$-\ 2,383$	$-\ 3,950$	$-\ 300$	$-\ 1,893$

Mixed Review

Regroup 1 hundred for 10 tens. You may use place-value blocks or draw a picture to help.

7. $345 = 2$ hundreds, _____ tens, 5 ones
   (4-5)

8. $789 = 6$ hundreds, _____ tens, 9 ones
   (4-5)

9. Write a time that is between midnight and half past twelve at night.
   (2-12)

   _____

Write each number in standard form.

10. $600,000 + 7,000 + 400 + 3$ _____
   (2-4)

11. four hundred thousand, eight hundred thirty _____
   (2-4)

Daily Cumulative Review

Write what number you would add to each in order to subtract mentally. Subtract. *(Lesson 4-14)*

1. 58 − 29 = _____

I added _____.

2. 32 − 17 _____

I added _____.

3. 73 − 38 = _____

I added _____.

4. 178 − 59 = _____

I added _____.

Solve each problem. *(Lesson 4-13)*

5. It costs $4 for a child's ticket and $7 for an adult's ticket to the amusement park. Chad is going to the park with his three sisters and his mother. Chad and his 3 sisters can each get child's tickets. How much will the total cost be?

_____

6. Susan sold 43 raffle tickets and 18 game tickets. How many more raffle tickets did she sell than game tickets?

_____

Mixed Review

Find each sum or difference.

7.
(4-11)
$$\begin{array}{r} 6\,0\,7 \\ -\ 2\,6\,6 \\ \hline \end{array}$$

8.
(4-12)
$$\begin{array}{r} \$2,6\,7\,0 \\ -\ \ \ 9\,7\,0 \\ \hline \end{array}$$

9.
(3-8)
$$\begin{array}{r} 4,9\,3\,7 \\ +\ 3,5\,1\,8 \\ \hline \end{array}$$

10.
(3-15)
$$\begin{array}{r} \$5.6\,7 \\ +\ 3.2\,9 \\ \hline \end{array}$$

11. Marcy buys a toy worth $3.27. She pays with $5.00. List which
(3-14) coins and bills you would use to make change. Then write the change in dollars and cents.

_____

_____

12. I am a 2-digit number. If you add me to 4,
(3-3) you will get a sum of 21. What number am I? _____

Name _____

Daily Cumulative Review

Subtract. *(Lesson 4-15)*

1. $9.0 0
      − 6.7 8

2. $5.7 5
      − 3.2 5

3. $2 0.0 0
      − 6.0 8

4. $6.9 8
      − 3.7 9

Write what number you would add to each in order to subtract mentally. Subtract *(Lesson 4-14)*

5. 82 − 35 = _____

I added _____.

6. 31 − 7 = _____

I added _____.

7. 177 − 37 = _____

I added _____.

8. 134 − 28 = _____

I added _____.

Mixed Review

Write the total value in cents or dollars and cents.

9.
(3-12)

10.
(3-13)

_____ _____

11. What is the greatest possible sum using three of these numbers?
(3-9)

87   741   390   123   500

_____

Find each sum using mental math.

12. $500 + $300 = _____
(3-1)

13. 700 + 600 = _____
(3-1)

Daily Cumulative Review

Use objects to solve each problem. *(Lesson 4-16)*

1. Jessica and her sister are helping their mother fold napkins. Jessica folds 3 napkins for every one napkin her sister folds.

   a. When Jessica has folded 9 napkins, how many napkins has her sister folded? _____

   b. When Jessica has folded 12 napkins, how many napkins has her sister folded? _____

2. Eric went on a class field trip to a wildlife park. Eric saw 3 times as many ducks as eagles. If Eric saw 6 eagles, how many ducks did he see? _____

3. Rhonda is at the end of the lunch line. There are 7 people ahead of her. Three people leave the line without buying anything. Two people buy their lunches and go to their seats. How many people are ahead of her now? _____

Subtract. *(Lesson 4-15)*

4. $5.76
   − 2.45

5. $18.00
   − 8.64

6. $9.32
   − 3.29

7. $14.00
   − 7.85

8. $7.50 − $3.27 = _____

9. $19.95 − $8.78 = _____

10. Drew bought a notebook for $2.19. He gave the clerk $5.00. How much change did he receive? _____

Mixed Review

11. "This movie lasts for 1 hour and 45 minutes," says Marc.
    (2-13) If it begins at 6:00 P.M., what time will the movie end?

    _____

12. What basic fact could you use to find 1,200 − 600? Solve.
    (4-2)

    _____

13. Write two numbers that add to 60 without regrouping.
    (3-6)

    _____

Daily Cumulative Review

Complete. *(Lesson 5-1)*

1. ⬭⬭⬭⬭⬭⬭
⬭⬭⬭⬭⬭

  a. _____ + _____ = _____

  b. _____ rows of _____ equals _____.

2. ⬭⬭ ⬭⬭ ⬭⬭
⬭⬭ ⬭⬭ ⬭⬭

  a. _____ + _____ + _____ = _____

  b. _____ groups of _____ equals _____.

Solve. Use objects to help. *(Lesson 4-16)*

3. Kathy has 8 coins in her pocket. She has $1.00 in all. What coins does she have in her pocket?

  _____

4. A fishing boat travels 1 mile out to sea. It took 15 minutes. How long should it take the boat to travel 4 miles?

  _____

Mixed Review

Solve. Check each answer.

5. (4-12)	**6.** (4-12)	**7.** (4-12)	**8.** (4-12)
3,214 − 1,113	$5,247 − 2,316	4,400 − 3,000	8,976 − 3,560

Estimate each difference.

9. $854 - 115 =$ _____
(4-4)

10. $775 - 93 =$ _____
(4-4)

11. $787 - 182 =$ _____
(4-4)

12. $207 - 128 =$ _____
(4-4)

13. $690 - 278 =$ _____
(4-4)

14. $6.81 - $3.85 =$ _____
(4-4)

Daily Cumulative Review

Complete each number sentence. *(Lesson 5-2)*

1.

(coins diagram: 3 rows of 4 ovals)

a. _____ + _____ + _____ + _____ = _____

b. _____ × _____ = _____

2. Can you multiply to find the total of 7 + 7 + 7? Explain.

_____

3. Can you multiply to find the total of 4 + 5 + 6? Explain.

_____

Write the next three numbers in each pattern. Then write the rule used to make the pattern. *(Lesson 5-1)*

4. 8, 16, 24, 32, _____, _____, _____

Rule: _____

Mixed Review

Subtract. Check each answer.

5.
(4-10)
$$446 - 267$$

6.
(4-10)
$$272 - 94$$

7.
(4-10)
$$325 - 76$$

8.
(4-10)
$$914 - 439$$

9. What is 683 minus 417? _____
(4-11)

10. Subtract 238 from 500. _____
(4-11)

11. Find the sum of $2.38 and $6.75. _____
(3-15)

12. Add $7.42 and $2.38. _____
(3-15)

Daily Cumulative Review

Write a multiplication story for 1–2. You may use counters to solve. *(Lesson 5-3)*

1. 3×5

_____

_____

2. 6×6

_____

_____

Draw a picture that shows 3 × 6. Find the product. *(Lesson 5-2)*

Mixed Review

3. Use front-end estimation to estimate the sum of 313, 579, and 404.
(3-16)

_____

4. Use front-end estimation to estimate the sum of $7.24, $4.69, and $9.61.
(3-16)

_____

Find each difference. You may use a hundred chart to help.

5. $93 - 37 =$ _____
(4-3)

6. $84 - $66 =$ _____
(4-3)

7. Maria has read 17 pages of her 62-page book. How many more pages does she have left to read? _____
(4-6)

Daily Cumulative Review

Find each product. *(Lesson 5-4)*

1. 5
    × 2

2. 2
    × 9

3. 2
    × 8

4. 7
    × 2

5. 1
    × 2

6. 2
    × 6

7. 4
    × 2

8. 2
    × 2

Solve. *(Lesson 5-3)*

9. There are 7 jugglers at a circus. Each juggler is juggling 3 balls. How many balls are there?

_____

10. There are 4 bowls of apples. Each bowl has 5 apples. How many apples are there?

_____

Mixed Review

11. Amelia buys a necklace for $8.13. She pays with $10.00.
(3-14) List which coins and bills you would use to make change. Then write the change in dollars and cents.

_____

_____

12. If you buy 2 items that cost $4.78 each, will $10.00 be enough
(3-16) to buy both items? Explain.

_____

_____

13. Use the fewest coins to make 43 cents.
(3-12)

_____

Daily Cumulative Review

Find each product. *(Lesson 5-5)*

1. $5 \times 3 =$ _____

2. $4 \times 5 =$ _____

3. $2 \times 8 =$ _____

4. $5 \times 7 =$ _____

5. Suppose you have 8 nickels in your pocket. How much money do you have?

_____

6. A swimming pool has 5 lanes. There are 5 swimmers in each lane. How many swimmers are there?

_____

Solve. *(Lesson 5-4)*

7. Find the product of 9 and 2. _____

8. Find the product of 4 and 2. _____

Mixed Review

Write each time in two ways.

9.
(2-11)

10.
(2-11)

_____   _____

11. The bus stops and 5 children get on. Now there are fifteen
(4-1) children on the bus. How many were on the bus before this stop?

_____

Estimate each difference.

12. $788 - 111 =$ _____
(4-4)

13. $\$5.99 - \$2.87 =$ _____
(4-4)

14. $517 - 182 =$ _____
(4-4)

15. $\$6.04 - \$1.12 =$ _____
(4-4)

Daily Cumulative Review

Use a hundred chart to complete the table. *(Lesson 5-6)*

1.

×	1	2	3	4	5	6	7	8	9
2									
5									

Solve. *(Lesson 5-5)*

2. Eva rides her horse 2 hours every day. How many hours does she ride in 5 days?

_____

3. Is 5 × 5 greater or less than 6 × 5? Explain.

_____

_____

Mixed Review

Write the total value in cents.

4.
(3-12)

5.
(3-12)

_____   _____

Find each difference.

6. 32 − 14 = _____
(4-3)

7. 64 − 48 = _____
(4-3)

Solve.

8. 5,332 − 2,100 = _____
(4-12)

9. $5,266 − $1,931 = _____
(4-12)

10. 1,384 + 1,600 = _____
(3-8)

11. $4,680 + $1,853 = _____
(3-8)

Daily Cumulative Review

Find each product. *(Lesson 5-7)*

1. $7 \times 0 =$ _____   **2.** $9 \times 1 =$ _____   **3.** $0 \times 3 =$ _____

4.   5   **5.**   5   **6.**   1   **7.**   0
     $\times\,1$ $\times\,2$ $\times\,9$ $\times\,0$

What multiple do each of these shaded patterns represent?
(Lesson 5-6)

8. Multiples of _____

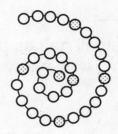

9. Multiples of _____

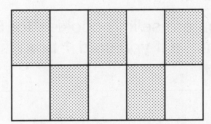

10. Multiples of _____

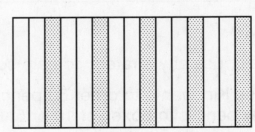

Mixed Review

Compare. Use <, >, or =.

11. 33 ◯ 31
(2-6)

12. 1,223 ◯ 2,567
(2-6)

Find each difference. You may use place-value blocks or
draw a picture to help.

13. $186 - 118 =$ _____
(4-8)

14. $145 - 79 =$ _____
(4-8)

Daily Cumulative Review

Find each product. *(Lesson 5-8)*

1. $9 \times 3 =$ _____   **2.** $9 \times 6 =$ _____   **3.** $7 \times 9 =$ _____

4. 4   **5.** 6   **6.** 9   **7.** 2
    $\times\ 9$ $\times\ 5$ $\times\ 9$ $\times\ 0$

8. The Rodriguez family goes skiing for 9 days every winter. How many days have they spent skiing in the past 5 years?

_____

9. Darin played in 6 basketball games this season. If he made 9 freethrows in each game, how many total freethrows did he make?

_____

Solve. *(Lesson 5-7)*

10. Suppose you are selling cookies for $6 a box. How much money would you make if you sold 1 box? If you sold 0 boxes? Explain.

_____

_____

Mixed Review

Make a list or use any strategy to help solve each part.

11. Suppose Kirt wants to order 50 pencils for the office. He
(2-5)   can buy pencils in boxes of 10 or 5. How many ways could he order exactly 50 pencils?

a.

boxes of 10						
boxes of 5						

b. How many ways are there? _____ ways

12. Find the difference of 40 and 16. _____
(4-7)

Daily Cumulative Review

**Decide if the problem has too much or too little information.
Then solve. If there is not enough information, tell what
information is needed.** *(Lesson 5-9)*

1. Susan lives 3 miles from school. She is planning a halloween party for 8 of her classmates. If each person drinks two cups of punch, how many cups of punch will Susan need to make altogether?

   Too much or too little information? _____

   How do you solve it? _____

   _____

2. The price of admission to an arts and crafts festival is $5.00. Mr. Ramirez would like to take his family to the festival this weekend. What will the total cost of admission be?

   Too much or too little information? _____

   How do you solve it? _____

   _____

   _____

Solve. *(Lesson 5-8)*

3. Find the product of 6 and 9. _____

4. Multiply 9 by 3. _____

Mixed Review

Find each difference.

5. 38 − 27 = _____
   (4-6)

6. $54 − $8 = _____
   (4-6)

7. Recess begins at 1:40 P.M. and ends at 1:55 P.M.
   (3-17) How many minutes is recess?   _____

8. Lunch lasts 45 minutes. If it begins at 12:30 P.M.,
   (3-17) when does lunch end?   _____

Name _____

Daily Cumulative Review

Draw a picture to help you solve. *(Lesson 5-10)*

1. Jason has 12 coins in his pocket. There are twice as many nickels as quarters. How many nickels does Jason have?

   _____

Decide if the problem has too much or too little information. Then solve. *(Lesson 5-9)*

2. A Rocky Mountain bighorn sheep weighs about 220 pounds and can move up to 30 feet in one leap down a steep cliff. How many feet could a bighorn sheep move in 2 leaps?

   Too much or too little information? _____

   How do you solve it? _____

   _____

Mixed Review

Subtract. Check each answer.

3. 352
(4-9) − 134

4. 579
(4-9) − 397

5. $294
(4-9) − 285

6. 96
(4-7) − 48

Write what number you would add to in order to subtract mentally. Subtract.

7. 44 − 29 = _____
(4-14)

   I added _____ to _____.

8. 97 − 28 = _____
(4-14)

   I added _____ to _____.

Name _____

Daily Cumulative Review

Find each product. *(Lesson 6-1)*

1.
$$
\begin{array}{r}
7 \\
\times\ 3 \\
\hline
\end{array}
$$

2.
$$
\begin{array}{r}
3 \\
\times\ 1 \\
\hline
\end{array}
$$

3.
$$
\begin{array}{r}
6 \\
\times\ 3 \\
\hline
\end{array}
$$

4.
$$
\begin{array}{r}
3 \\
\times\ 9 \\
\hline
\end{array}
$$

5. 5×3

6. 3×2

7. 8×3

8. 3×4

9. If you know the product of 2×7, how can you find the product of 3×7? What is it?

_____

Draw a picture or use any strategy to solve the problem. *(Lesson 5-10)*

10. The soccer coach has 18 shin guards, 13 jerseys, and 10 soccer balls. If there are 10 players on the soccer team, does the coach have enough equipment so that each player can have 2 shin guards, 1 jersey, and 1 soccer ball.

_____

Mixed Review

11. Sarah is buying shampoo. Regular shampoo costs $3.78
(4-15) and shampoo with conditioner costs $6.55. How much will she save if she buys regular shampoo?

_____

Daily Cumulative Review

Find each product. *(Lesson 6-2)*

1. 6
× 4

2. 4
× 3

3. 1
× 4

4. 5
× 4

5. Multiply 9 by 4.

_____

6. Multiply 4 by 2.

_____

7. Draw arrays to show that 4 × 8 is the same as 8 × 4.

Find each product. *(Lesson 6-1)*

8. 3 × 8 = _____

9. 3 × 3 = _____

10. Scientists can tell the speed of a dinosaur from the space
between the footprints it left behind. Large dinosaurs ran
4 miles in one hour. Smaller dinosaurs ran about 3 times
faster. How fast did the smaller dinosaurs run?

_____

Mixed Review

Add.

11.
(3-9)
  6 4
  9 1
+   8

12.
(3-9)
  3 1 2
  1 7 4
+   3 6

13.
(3-9)
  7 8 0
  4 1 2
+   1 2

14.
(3-9)
    6 6
    5 0 8
+ 2 2 4

Use mental math to find each sum.

15. 80 + 65 = _____
(3-11)

16. 57 + 9 = _____
(3-11)

Daily Cumulative Review

Find each product. *(Lesson 6-3)*

1. $\begin{array}{r} 1 \\ \times\ 6 \\ \hline \end{array}$

2. $\begin{array}{r} 7 \\ \times\ 6 \\ \hline \end{array}$

3. $\begin{array}{r} 6 \\ \times\ 3 \\ \hline \end{array}$

4. $\begin{array}{r} 5 \\ \times\ 6 \\ \hline \end{array}$

5. Which is greater, 7×9 or 9×6? How can you tell without multiplying?

_____

_____

6. Can you think of a way to use doubling to multiply 6×8? Explain.

_____

_____

7. You need enough hotdog buns for 58 people. Each package has 6 buns. Are 9 packages enough? Explain.

_____

_____

Find each product. *(Lesson 6-2)*

8. $\begin{array}{r} 8 \\ \times\ 4 \\ \hline \end{array}$

9. $\begin{array}{r} 4 \\ \times\ 2 \\ \hline \end{array}$

10. $\begin{array}{r} 4 \\ \times\ 0 \\ \hline \end{array}$

11. $\begin{array}{r} 9 \\ \times\ 4 \\ \hline \end{array}$

12. Jennifer receives 4 report cards every year. How many report cards does she receive in 4 years?

_____

Mixed Review.

Guess and check to solve.

13. The Hawks beat the Jays in a baseball game. The scores
(3-10) were 4 runs apart and there were 18 runs scored in the game. How many runs did each team score?

_____

Name _____

Daily Review
6-5

Daily Cumulative Review

Find each product. *(Lesson 6-4)*

1. 6
$\times$ 7

2. 8
$\times$ 8

3. 7
$\times$ 9

4. 5
$\times$ 8

5. 0×8

6. 7×8

7. 2×8

8. 7×3

_____

9. A small restaurant has 8 tables. Each table can seat up to 8 people. How many people can eat in the restaurant at one time?

_____

Find each product. *(Lesson 6-3)*

10. 6×6

11. 6×3

12. 8×6

13. 1×6

_____

14. A trolley makes a trip around an amusement park every 6 minutes. How many minutes does it take the trolley to make 7 trips around the park.

_____

Mixed Review

15. Do these counters show equal groups? Explain.
₍₅₋₁₎

_____

Add. Estimate to check.

16. $\$2.34 + \$1.71 =$ _____
₍₃₋₁₅₎

17. $\$5.72 + 2.68 =$ _____
₍₃₋₁₅₎

Subtract. Check each answer.

18. $640 - 228 =$ _____
₍₄₋₁₁₎

19. $605 - 438 =$ _____
₍₄₋₁₁₎

74

Daily Cumulative Review

Use decision making to solve. *(Lesson 6-5)*

Dave is a group leader for an outdoor adventure club. He must order the supplies for 3 trips—one for 4 people, one for 6 people, and one for 9 people.

Complete the table.

Number per person	4-Person Trip	6-Person Trip	9-Person Trip
6 potatoes	24	36	54
3 cans of tuna fish			
2 boxes of oatmeal			
7 apples			
8 bananas			
1 loaf of bread			
9 eggs			

1. How many eggs will Dave need for the 9-person trip? _____

2. How many cans of tuna fish will he need for the
   6-person trip?   _____

Find each product. *(Lesson 6-4)*

3. 9×8 **4.** 7×7 **5.** 4×7

_____   _____   _____

Mixed Review

Round to the nearest hundred.

6. 337 _____   **7.** 673 _____   **8.** $212 _____
(2-9)   *(2-9)*   *(2-9)*

9. Find the difference of 487 and 192. _____
(4-9)

Daily Cumulative Review

Find each missing number. You may use this portion of a hundred chart to help. *(Lesson 6-6)*

1	2	3	4	5	6	7	8	9	10
11	12	13	14	15	16	17	18	19	20
21	22	23	24	25	26	27	28	29	30
31	32	33	34	35	36	37	38	39	40
41	42	43	44	45	46	47	48	49	50
51	52	53	54	55	56	57	58	59	60

1. $4 \times \boxed{} = 24$

2. $\boxed{} \times 3 = 12$

3. $7 \times \boxed{} = 42$

4. $\boxed{} \times 9 = 27$

Solve the problem. *(Lesson 6-5)*

5. A well balanced diet includes 4 servings of vegetables a day. How many servings of vegetables should a person eat in 5 days?

_____

Mixed Review

6. Write the total value in dollars and cents. _____
(3-13)

Add. Estimate to check.

7. $\$6.27$
(3-15) $+\ 1.59$

8. $\$9.60$
(3-15) $+\ 4.75$

9. $\$0.34$
(3-15) $+\ 2.93$

10. $\$3.97$
(3-15) $+\ 3.45$

Daily Cumulative Review

Find each product. *(Lesson 6-7)*

1. 10×0 **2.** 11×12 **3.** 8×12

_____   _____   _____

4. 8×10 **5.** 5×12 **6.** 4×8

_____   _____   _____

7. 12×4 **8.** 5×11 **9.** 10×10

_____   _____   _____

Write true or false. If the answer is false, explain why. *(Lesson 6-6)*

10. 44 is a multiple of 3.

_____

_____

11. 36 is a multiple of 3 and 6.

_____

_____

Mixed Review

Subtract. Check each answer.

12.   5,6 7 8
(4-12) $-$ 4,7 7 1

13.   4,1 0 0
(4-12) $-$ 2,6 0 0

14.   8,6 5 0
(4-12) $-$ 4,3 3 1

15. $1,6 7 1
(4-12) $-$ 5 0 0

16. $4.7 7
(4-15) $-$ 2.2 6

17. $7.4 1
(4-15) $-$ 3.6 5

18. $1 2.0 0
(4-15) $-$ 5.8 6

19. $3 0.0 0
(4-15) $-$ 9.9 8

Daily Cumulative Review

Find each product. *(Lesson 6-8)*

1. $(3 \times 3) \times 2$

2. $(5 \times 2) \times 1$

3. $(0 \times 9) \times 8$

_____

_____

_____

4. $(4 \times 2) \times 9$

5. $(7 \times 1) \times 7$

6. $(2 \times 3) \times 5$

_____

_____

_____

7. Find the product of 1, 8, and 9. _____

8. Darin and Edward play on the same soccer team. They played in 5 soccer games this season and they each scored 2 goals in every game. How many goals did Darin and Edward score for the team altogether?

_____

Find each product. *(Lesson 6-7)*

9. 10×9

10. 11×7

11. 12×5

_____

_____

_____

12. 0×12

13. 8×11

14. 12×7

_____

_____

_____

Mixed Review

Find each missing number. You may use a hundred chart to help.

15. $76 - \_\_\_\_ = 31$
(4-3)

16. $\_\_\_\_ - 42 = 8$
(4-3)

17. $98 - \_\_\_\_ = 86$
(4-3)

18. $\_\_\_\_ - 22 = 19$
(4-3)

19. Find the product of 12 and 1. _____
(5-7)

20. Multiply 0 by 8. _____
(5-7)

21. Find the product of 6 and 9. _____
(5-8)

22. Multiply 9 by 3. _____
(5-8)

Daily Cumulative Review

Use any strategy to solve each problem. *(Lesson 6-9)*

1. Suppose you are planning a picnic for 52 people. You must buy plastic forks in packages of 6. How many packages of plastic forks will you need?

   _____

2. You are making pasta salad for a party. Each package of pasta is enough for 7 servings.

   a. If 82 people are at the party, how many packages of pasta should you use so that each person gets one serving?

   _____

   b. How many servings will be left over?

   _____

Find each product. *(Lesson 6-8)*

3. $(2 \times 2) \times 8$ **4.** $(1 \times 12) \times 2$ **5.** $(2 \times 9) \times 1$

_____   _____   _____

6. $2 \times (5 \times 3)$ **7.** $7 \times 1 \times 7$ **8.** $2 \times (3 \times 8)$

_____   _____   _____

9. Find the product of 8, 5, and 0. _____

Mixed Review

Write a multiplication story. You may use counters to solve.

10. 4×5
(5-3)

_____

_____

11. Multiply 6 by 3. _____   **12.** Multiply 9 by 3. _____
(6-1)   (6-1)

Daily Cumulative Review

Use any strategy to solve the problem. *(Lesson 7-1)*

Mr. Lazari raises turkeys. He has 9 turkeys in all. He wants to put the turkeys into 3 pens so that there is an equal number of birds in each pen. How many birds should he put in each pen?

1. Draw rings to divide the turkeys into 3 equal groups.

2. 9 Turkeys ÷ 3 pens = _____ turkeys each.

Use any strategy to solve the problem. *(Lesson 6-9)*

3. Your hockey team has a party. Everyone eats 3 slices of pizza. If there are 14 people at the party, how many slices of pizza were eaten?   _____

Mixed Review

Find each product.

4.
(6-2)
```
  8
× 4
```

5.
(6-2)
```
  4
× 4
```

6.
(6-2)
```
  7
× 4
```

7.
(6-2)
```
  2
× 4
```

8.
(5-7)
```
  9
× 0
```

9.
(5-7)
```
  1
× 6
```

10.
(5-7)
```
  0
× 0
```

11.
(5-7)
```
  0
× 1
```

Name _____

Daily Cumulative Review

Complete. You may use counters or complete the pictures to help. *(Lesson 7-2)*

1. 12 people
3 in each boat

12 ÷ 3 = _____

2. 15 roses
5 in each vase

15 ÷ 5 = _____

Complete. You may use counters or draw pictures to help. *(Lesson 7-1)*

3. A class of 16 children is on a field trip to a wetlands nature preserve. There are 4 guides at the nature preserve. How should the tracker divide up the class so that every guide works with the same number of children?

_____

4. Mrs. Logan bought 15 pencils for her 3 children. If she divides them equally, how many pencils should each child get?

_____

Mixed Review

Find each product.

5. 6 × 2 = _____
(5-4)

6. 2 × 10 = _____
(5-4)

7. 7 × 5 = _____
(5-5)

8. 5 × 5 = _____
(5-5)

9. 8 × 5 = _____
(5-5)

10. 5 × 1 = _____
(5-5)

Daily Cumulative Review

Solve. You may use counters or draw pictures to help. *(Lesson 7-3)*

1. Denise has 24 free show tickets. She can give away 4 to each of her little brothers. How many brothers does she have?

   _____

2. David needs to frame 12 paintings. He frames 3 paintings each day. How long will it take him to finish?

   _____

3. A baker uses 27 cups of flour to make 9 equal-sized cakes. How many cups of flour did he use for each cake?

   _____

Draw a picture to help you solve. *(Lesson 7-2)*

4. Florence puts 3 cookies on each plate. Can she make 6 plates with 18 cookies? Explain.

   _____

   _____

Mixed Review

Find each product.

5. $3 \times 5 =$ _____
(5-5)

6. $5 \times 6 =$ _____
(5-5)

7. $\begin{array}{r} 9 \\ \times\ 7 \\ \hline \end{array}$
(5-8)

8. $\begin{array}{r} 8 \\ \times\ 9 \\ \hline \end{array}$
(5-8)

9. $\begin{array}{r} 3 \\ \times\ 9 \\ \hline \end{array}$
(5-8)

10. $\begin{array}{r} 5 \\ \times\ 9 \\ \hline \end{array}$
(5-8)

Daily Cumulative Review

Complete. You may use counters to help. *(Lesson 7-4)*

1. $7 \times$ _____ $= 14$

$14 \div 7 =$ _____

2. $4 \times$ _____ $= 16$

$16 \div 4 =$ _____

3. $5 \times$ _____ $= 40$

$40 \div 5 =$ _____

4. $3 \times$ _____ $= 18$

$18 \div 3 =$ _____

5. $7 \times$ _____ $= 21$

$21 \div 7 =$ _____

6. $6 \times$ _____ $= 36$

$36 \div 6 =$ _____

7. What multiplication fact could you use to solve $20 \div 4$?

_____

Write a division story for each. *(Lesson 7-3)*

8. $18 \div 3$

_____

_____

9. $25 \div 5$

_____

_____

Mixed Review

10. Can you multiply to find the total of $8 + 8 + 8$? Explain.
(5-2)

_____

11. Can you multiply to find the total of $4 + 6 + 7$? Explain.
(5-2)

_____

12. Find the product of 7 and 9.
(6-4)

_____

13. Find the product of 8 and 6.
(6-4)

_____

14. Continue this pattern. 128, 117, 106, _____, _____, _____
(6-7)

Name _____

Daily Cumulative Review

Find each quotient. *(Lesson 7-5)*

1. 2)1 4   **2.** 2)8   **3.** 2)2 0   **4.** 2)1 2

5. Divide 16 by 2. _____   **6.** Divide 10 by 2. _____

7. Kendra has 24 trees in her backyard. Half of these are apple trees. How many apple trees are there?

_____

8. Peter buys 26 dog bones for the dogs at the kennel. If each dog gets 2 bones, how many dogs are in the kennel?

_____

Complete. You may use counters to help. *(Lesson 7-4)*

9. $15 \div 5 =$ _____   **10.** $35 \div 7 =$ _____

    $5 \times$ _____ $= 15$ $7 \times$ _____ $= 35$

11. a. What multiplication fact could you use to solve $18 \div 3$?   _____

    b. $18 \div 3 =$ _____

Mixed Review

12. Write each time in two ways. Write A.M. or P.M.
(2-12)

 breakfast time

_____

13. Draw a picture to help you solve. How many bricks will Brian need to build a garden wall 7 bricks long and 6 bricks high?
(5-10)

_____

Daily Cumulative Review

Find each quotient. *(Lesson 7-6)*

1. 5)4 5　　　　**2.** 5)2 0　　　　**3.** 5)4 0　　　　**4.** 5)1 5

5. 25 ÷ 5 = _____　　　　**6.** 10 ÷ 5 = _____

7. 30 ÷ 5 = _____　　　　**8.** 35 ÷ 5 = _____

Find each quotient. *(Lesson 7-5)*

9. 2)1 6　　　**10.** 2)1 0　　　**11.** 2)6　　　**12.** 2)1 8

13. How can you use multiplication to help you find 20 ÷ 2?

_____

_____

Mixed Review

Decide if the problem has too much or too little information.
Then solve. If there is not enough information, tell what
information is needed.

14. A polar bear weighs about 1,000 pounds. It is an excellent
(5-9) swimmer. The black bear weighs about 400 pounds. About
how much more does a polar bear weigh than a black bear?

Too much or too little information? _____

How do you solve it? _____

Subtract. Check each answer.

15.　　5 3 9　　　**16.**　　$3 4 5　　　**17.**　　2 2 0　　　**18.**　　9 6
(4-9)　− 2 4 8　　*(4-9)*　− 1 2 7　　*(4-9)*　−　7 5　　*(4-9)*　− 5 4

Name _____

Daily Cumulative Review

Find each quotient. *(Lesson 7-7)*

1. 4)2 0　　　　　　　　　　**2.** 3)2 1

3. 4)1 6　　　　　　　　　　**4.** 3)2 7

5. How many 4s are in 16? _____

6. How many 3s are in 18? _____

Find each quotient. *(Lesson 7-6)*

7. 40 ÷ 5 = _____　　　　**8.** 15 ÷ 5 = _____

9. 35 ÷ 5 = _____　　　　**10.** 25 ÷ 5 = _____

11. 45 ÷ 5 = _____　　　　**12.** 20 ÷ 5 = _____

Mixed Review

13. Debbie takes her dog to the beach and lets him run for
(2-13) 25 minutes. If she lets him loose at 10:30 A.M., what time
should she call the dog back?

_____

14. Continue the pattern. Then write the rule.
(4-2)

In	60	70	80	90	100	110
Out	35	45	55			

Rule: _____

15. One bottle of juice can fill 8 glasses. How many bottles
(6-9) of juice will you need to fill 28 glasses?

_____

Name _____

Daily Cumulative Review

Find each quotient. *(Lesson 7-8)*

1. 4 ÷ 1 = _____

2. 0 ÷ 3 = _____

3. 6 ÷ 6 = _____

4. 9 ÷ 1 = _____

5. 0 ÷ 8 = _____

6. 9 ÷ 9 = _____

7. 7 ÷ 1 = _____

8. 0 ÷ 5 = _____

Find each quotient. *(Lesson 7-7)*

9. 12 ÷ 4 = _____

10. 27 ÷ 3 = _____

11. 21 ÷ 3 = _____

12. 16 ÷ 4 = _____

13. 36 ÷ 4 = _____

14. 6 ÷ 3 = _____

15. Ellen brought 18 pieces of chicken to the picnic.
If 3 people are at the picnic, how many pieces
can each person eat?

_____

Mixed Review

Find each product.

16. (3 × 2) × 4
(6-8)

17. 1 × (7 × 6)
(6-8)

18. 6 × (9 × 0)
(6-8)

_____   _____   _____

19. 5 × 2 × 2
(6-8)

20. 1 × (7 × 3)
(6-8)

21. 6 × (4 × 2)
(6-8)

_____   _____   _____

22. What multiplication fact could you use to solve 32 ÷ 4?
(7-4)

_____

23. How can you use multiplication to help you find 16 ÷ 2?
(7-5)

_____

Daily Cumulative Review

Which number sentence would you use to solve the problem? Explain. *(Lesson 7-9)*

1. Suppose Brett worked 8 hours a week for 4 weeks. How many hours did he work?

  A. $8 - 4 = 4$ **B.** $8 + 4 = 12$ **C.** $8 \div 4 = 2$ **D.** $8 \times 4 = 32$

_____

2. Stephen had 12 newspapers. He delivered 6 of them. How many did he have left?

  A. $12 - 6 = 6$ **B.** $12 + 6 = 18$ **C.** $12 \times 6 = 72$ **D.** $12 \div 6 = 2$

_____

3. Jesper makes kites. He has 15 kites in his garage. He gave an equal number of them to each of 5 friends. How many kites did each friend get?

  A. $15 + 5 = 20$ **B.** $15 \div 5 = 3$ **C.** $15 \times 5 = 75$ **D.** $15 - 5 = 10$

_____

Find each quotient. *(Lesson 7-8)*

4. $8\overline{)8}$ **5.** $1\overline{)7}$ **6.** $2\overline{)0}$

Mixed Review

Find each answer.

7. $\$7.72 + \$4.15 =$ _____
(3-15)

8. $365 - 127 =$ _____
(4-9)

9. $843 - 755 =$ _____
(4-10)

10. $\$12.50 - \$6.99 =$ _____
(4-15)

11. $5 \times 12 =$ _____
(6-7)

12. $12 \times 11 =$ _____
(6-7)

13. Divide 16 by 4. _____
(7-7)

14. Divide 20 by 5. _____
(7-6)

Daily Cumulative Review

Find each quotient. *(Lesson 7-10)*

1. $6\overline{)4\,2}$

2. $7\overline{)1\,4}$

3. $7\overline{)6\,3}$

4. $6\overline{)4\,8}$

5. $6 \div 6 =$ _____

6. $35 \div 7 =$ _____

7. Is the quotient of $54 \div 6$ greater or less than the quotient of $49 \div 7$? Explain.

_____

Write which operation you would use. Then solve.
(Lesson 7-9)

8. Maria bought a gallon of milk for $1.85 and a bag of apples for $1.30. How much money did she spend?

_____

9. Hector and his family went on a backpacking trip. They hiked 3 miles a day for 9 days. How many miles did they hike?

_____

Mixed Review

10. Find the product of 6 and 7.
(6-3)

11. What is 6 multiplied by 4?
(6-3)

_____   _____

12. What is the pattern for multiples of 10?
(6-7)

_____

13. How can you use multiplication to find $12 \div 2$?
(7-5)

_____

Daily Cumulative Review

Find each quotient. *(Lesson 7-11)*

1. $8\overline{)40}$

2. $9\overline{)63}$

3. $9\overline{)9}$

4. $9\overline{)72}$

5. $32 \div 8 =$ _____

6. $54 \div 9 =$ _____

7. Divide 27 by 9. _____

8. Divide 48 by 8. _____

9. What multiplication fact can help you find $45 \div 9$?

_____

Find each quotient. *(Lesson 7-10)*

10. $6\overline{)18}$

11. $7\overline{)28}$

12. $6\overline{)30}$

13. It takes about 2 years for the planet Mars to make one orbit around the sun. How many orbits does the planet make in 6 years?

_____

Mixed Review

Find each product.

14. 6×8
₍₆₋₄₎

15. 0×7
₍₆₋₄₎

16. 8×4
₍₆₋₄₎

17. 7×8
₍₆₋₄₎

_____   _____   _____   _____

Find each missing number. You may use a hundred chart to help.

18. $6 \times \boxed{} = 36$
₍₆₋₆₎

19. $\boxed{} \times 3 = 9$
₍₆₋₆₎

Use any strategy to solve the problem.

20. One loaf of bread makes 14 sandwiches. How many
₍₆₋₉₎ loaves do you need to make 45 sandwiches?

_____

Name _____

Daily Cumulative Review

Write odd or even for each. You may use color cubes to help. *(Lesson 7-12)*

1. 4 _____

2. 16 _____

3. 13 _____

4. 26 _____

5. 5 _____

6. 27 _____

7. 28 _____

8. 13 _____

9. Todd has 2 shelves in his CD rack. He puts 5 CDs on one shelf and 11 CDs on the other shelf. Does he have an even or odd number of CDs? Explain.

_____

Find each quotient. *(Lesson 7-11)*

10. $72 \div 8 =$ _____

11. $81 \div 9 =$ _____

12. Divide 36 by 9. _____

13. Divide 64 by 8. _____

14. Which is greater, $56 \div 8$ or $63 \div 9$? _____

Mixed Review

Use any strategy to solve each problem.

15. You are making pizza for a party. Each pizza has 6 slices.
(6-9) If 70 people will be at the party, how many pizzas should you make so that each person gets one slice?

_____

16. One package of juice mix makes 2 gallons of juice. How
(6-9) many packages should you use to make 12 gallons?

_____

17. Divide 14 by 2. _____
(7-5)

18. Divide 8 by 2. _____
(7-5)

Find each quotient.

19. $27 \div 3 =$ _____
(7-7)

20. $21 \div 7 =$ _____
(7-10)

21. $24 \div 6 =$ _____
(7-10)

22. $16 \div 8 =$ _____
(7-11)

Daily Cumulative Review

Use any strategy to solve. *(Lesson 7-13)*

1. Kristin took 16 photographs while on vacation. She wants to place the pictures in her album so that each page has an equal number of pictures.

   a. How many pages could Kristin use?

   _____

   b. How many photographs could be on each page?

   _____

   c. List all the ways Kristin could put the photographs in her album.

   _____

   _____

You may use a hundreds chart to answer these questions. *(Lesson 7-12)*

2. What are the even numbers between
   0 and 30 that end in 4? _____

3. List the odd multiples of 7 that are less than 50. _____

4. Are the multiples of 8 even or odd? _____

Mixed Review

Solve. Check each answer.

5. *(4-12)*	**6.** *(4-12)*	**7.** *(4-12)*	**8.** *(4-12)*
$7{,}194$ $-\ 4{,}007$	$\$1{,}800$ $-\ \ \ 781$	$4{,}793$ $-\ 3{,}234$	$\$4{,}987$ $-\ 2{,}356$

Find each product.

9. *(5-8)*	**10.** *(5-8)*	**11.** *(5-8)*	**12.** *(5-8)*
9 $\times\ 8$	1 $\times\ 9$	9 $\times\ 4$	7 $\times\ 9$

Daily Cumulative Review

Find all the ways to balance the scale. Make a table to record each way. You may use color cubes to help.
(Lesson 7-14)

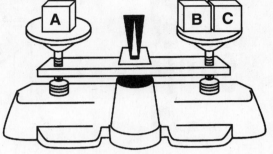

1. Box A has 9 cubes inside. How many cubes can be in boxes B and C?

Fill in the missing numbers in the table.

A	9	9	9	9	9	9	9	9	9	9
B	9	8								0
C	0		2	3						

Use any strategy to solve. *(Lesson 7-13)*

2. Patricia must read a 24-page book. She wants to read an equal number of pages every day. List all the possible ways she could divide her reading.

_____

_____

_____

Mixed Review

Find each product.

3. $9 \times 7 =$ _____
(5-8)

4. $3 \times 9 =$ _____
(5-8)

5. $9 \times 5 =$ _____
(5-8)

6. 8
(6-4) $\times 7$

7. 5
(6-4) $\times 8$

8. 7
(6-4) $\times 6$

9. 3
(6-4) $\times 7$

10. Four friends share an 8-pack of juice equally.
(7-3) How many cartons of juice does each one drink?

$8 \div 4 =$ _____ cartons

Daily Cumulative Review

Name the solid figure that each object looks like. *(Lesson 8-1)*

1.

2.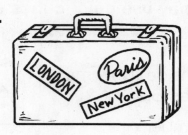

3.

_____ _____ _____

Find the way to balance the scale. You may use color cubes to help. *(Lesson 7-14)*

4. Box B has 6 cubes inside.
Box C has 8 cubes inside.
How many cubes are in
each box A?

_____

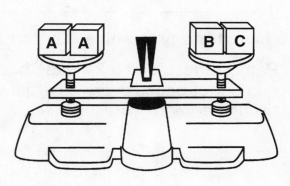

Mixed Review

Subtract. Check each answer.

5. 517 − 188 = _____
(4-10)

6. 273 − 69 = _____
(4-10)

7. 643 − 194 = _____
(4-10)

8. 312 − 59 = _____
(4-10)

Draw a picture or use any strategy to solve.

9. Ms. Gish has 4 balloons, 3 horns, and 3 hats to give
(5-10) out to 10 students as game prizes. She does not want
to give out the same prize twice in a row. In what
order should she hand out the three prize items?

_____

_____

Daily Cumulative Review

Name the shape that each object looks like. *(Lesson 8-2)*

1.

_____

2.

_____

3. What shape can you trace from this cylinder?

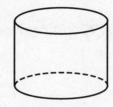

_____

Name the solid figure which answers the riddle.
Draw the figure in the space below the question. *(Lesson 8-1)*

4. I have 0 flat faces. I have 0 corners. What am I?

_____

Mixed Review

Solve. You may use counters or draw pictures to help.

5. Andrew and Ali have volunteered to call 12 people to
(7-1) raise money for their soccer league. If they divide the calls equally, how many calls will each boy make?

_____

6. There are 8 chairs around a table. Each chair has
(5-3) 4 legs. How many chair legs are there?

_____

Daily Cumulative Review

Complete each drawing. *(Lesson 8-3)*

1. Draw a ray.

2. Draw 2 intersecting lines.

Solve. Draw pictures to help. *(Lesson 8-2)*

3. How many sides does a triangle have? _____

4. How many sides does a circle have? _____

Mixed Review

Complete. You may use counters to help.

4. $3 \times$ _____ $= 21$ **5.** $5 \times$ _____ $= 30$ **6.** $7 \times$ _____ $= 49$
(7-4)   (7-4)   (7-4)

$21 \div 3 =$ _____ $30 \div 5 =$ _____ $49 \div 7 =$ _____

7. What multiplication fact could you use to solve $32 \div 8$?
(7-4)

_____

Find each missing number. Use a hundred chart to help.

8. $68 -$ _____ $= 31$ **9.** $84 -$ _____ $= 61$
(4-3)   (4-3)

10. _____ $- 27 = 58$ **11.** _____ $- 16 = 35$
(4-3)   (4-3)

Daily Cumulative Review

Write whether each angle is a right angle, less than a right angle, or greater than a right angle. *(Lesson 8-4)*

1.

2.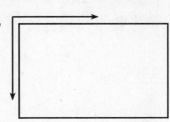

3.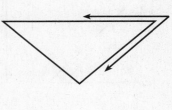

_____ _____ _____

Write the name for each. *(Lesson 8-3)*

4.

5.

6.

_____ _____ _____

Mixed Review

Find each quotient.

7. 4)‾16‾
(7-7)

8. 5)‾20‾
(7-7)

9. 4)‾24‾
(7-7)

10. 27 ÷ 3 = _____
(7-7)

11. 36 ÷ 4 = _____
(7-7)

Write which operation you would use. Then solve.

12. Lidia made 3 toy animals for each of her 4 friends.
(7-9) How many toy animals did she make in all?

_____

13. Ruth worked 4 hours before lunch and 5 hours
(7-9) after lunch. How many hours did she work in all?

_____

Daily Cumulative Review

Write slide, flip, or turn for each. *(Lesson 8-5)*

1.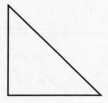

_____

2.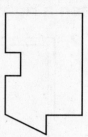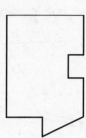

_____

Write whether each angle is a right angle, less than a right angle, or greater than a right angle. *(Lesson 8-4)*

3.

_____

4.

_____

5.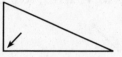

_____

Mixed Review

Write >, <, or =.

6. $7 \div 7 \bigcirc 3 \div 1$
(7-8)

7. $4 \div 2 \bigcirc 0 \div 8$
(7-8)

8. $9 \div 3 \bigcirc 3 \div 1$
(7-8)

9. $10 \div 2 \bigcirc 0 \div 5$
(7-8)

Continue each pattern.

10. 0, 12, 24, _____, _____, _____
(6-7)

11. 66, 55, 44, _____, _____, _____
(6-7)

12. 20, 40, 60, _____, _____, _____
(6-7)

13. Write a number between 3,812 and 4,003. _____
(2-7)

Daily Cumulative Review

Does each object appear to have a line of symmetry?
Write yes or no. *(Lesson 8-6)*

1.

_____

2.

_____

Color the figures that are congruent to the first figure red.
(Lesson 8-5)

3.

Mixed Review

Which number sentence would you use to solve the problem? Explain.

4. Suppose Larry worked 9 hours a week for 3 weeks.
(7-9) How many hours did he work?

    A. $9 - 3 = 6$ **B.** $9 + 3 = 12$ **C.** $9 \div 3 = 3$ **D.** $9 \times 3 = 27$

_____

5. Maria had 8 tickets to the basketball game. She gave
(7-9) 2 tickets to her friend, Rose. How many tickets did she
have left?

    A. $8 + 2 = 10$ **B.** $8 - 2 = 6$ **C.** $8 \times 2 = 16$ **D.** $8 \div 2 = 4$

_____

6. Draw a line segment.
(8-3)

Daily Cumulative Review

Use any strategy to solve each problem. *(Lesson 8-7)*

1. Four students are standing in a line. Jenny is behind Patricia. Juan is the only one between Ken and Jenny. Ken is behind Jenny. Who is the first in line?

_____

2. Jeff has 63 baseball cards. He gives nine to his friend and puts the rest into his album. He places the same number of cards on each page. If he uses six pages, how many cards are on each page?

_____

Which of these letters have no lines of symmetry? Explain.
(Lesson 8-6)

A B C D E F G

3. _____

_____

Mixed Review

Find each quotient.

4. $48 \div 6 =$ _____
(7-10)

5. $7 \div 7 =$ _____
(7-10)

6. $63 \div 7 =$ _____
(7-10)

7. $54 \div 9 =$ _____
(7-11)

8. $64 \div 8 =$ _____
(7-11)

9. $45 \div 9 =$ _____
(7-11)

Use any strategy to solve.

10. Jon walked 2 miles for every 1 mile his sister
(4-16) Janice walked. If Janice walked 3 miles, how many miles did Jon walk?

_____

11. Diego gave each of his six friends four cards.
(7-3) He made them at school. How many cards did he give away?

_____

Name _____

Daily Cumulative Review

Find the perimeter of each. *(Lesson 8-8)*

1.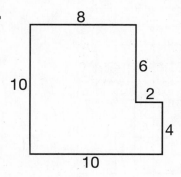

2.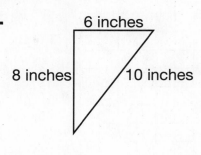

_____   _____

Use any strategy to solve the problem. *(Lesson 8-7)*

3. a. How many triangles can you find in this design?

_____

b. How many squares are in the design?

_____

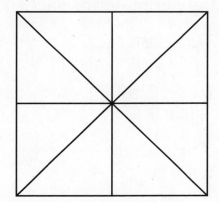

Mixed Review

Find each quotient.

4. 9)2 7
(7-11)

5. 8)0
(7-11)

6. 8)4 8
(7-11)

7. 81 ÷ 9 = _____
(7-11)

8. 72 ÷ 9 = _____
(7-11)

9. What multiplication fact can help you find 56 ÷ 7? _____
(7-10)

10. Bill's book has 21 pages. He reads 7 pages each day. How long will it take him to read the book? _____
(7-3)

Daily Cumulative Review

Find each area. Write your answer in square units. *(Lesson 8-9)*

1.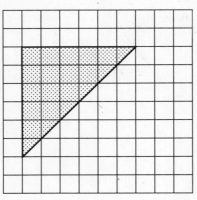

2.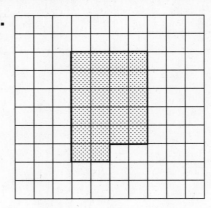

_____   _____

Find the perimeter of each. *(Lesson 8-8)*

3.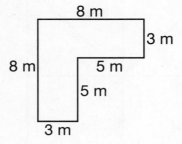

4.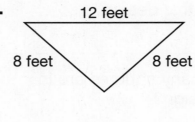

_____   _____

Mixed Review

5. Robert has 3 plates to hold a batch of cookies. He puts 6 cookies
(7-12) on each plate. Does he have an even or odd number of cookies?
Draw a picture and explain.

_____

6. Yasmin has 50¢. She wants to buy 3 pencils.
(4-3) Each pencil costs 20¢. How much more money
will she need to buy the pencils?   _____

Daily Cumulative Review

**You want to move a couch into your living room.
Do you have enough room?** *(Lesson 8-10)*

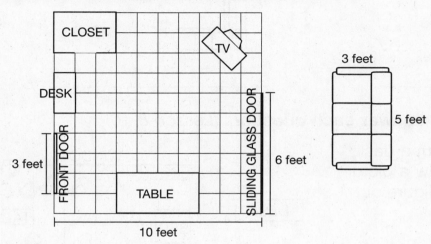

1. What do you know?

_____

2. Is there enough room for the couch?

_____

Find each area. Write your answer in square units. *(Lesson 8-9)*

3.

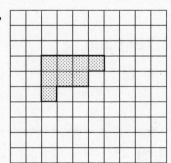

4.

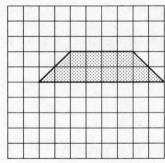

_____   _____

Mixed Review

Use any strategy to solve.

5. Suppose you are planning a picnic for 46 people. You must
(6-9) buy paper plates in packages of 12. How many packages
of paper plates will you need?

_____

Daily Cumulative Review

Find the volume of each. You may use cubes to help. *(Lesson 8-11)*

1. _____

2. _____

Use the drawing to answer each question. *(Lesson 8-10)*

Christine wants to put a desk in her room. She drew a picture of her room to help figure out where it will fit.

 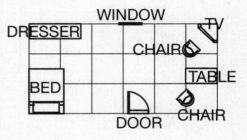

3. Does Christine have space for her desk? _____

4. Where could she put it? _____

Mixed Review

5. Find the product of 2, 6, and 1. _____
(6-8)

6. Does 8 × 3 have the same product as 4 × 2 × 3? Explain.
(6-8)

_____

_____

7. If you know the product of 2 × 7, how can you find
(6-1) the product of 3 × 7? What is it?

_____

8. Mark says, "To find 3 × 9, I can find 2 × 9 and add one
(6-1) more group of 2." What's wrong? Explain.

_____

Daily Cumulative Review

**Write the ordered pair. Answer
the questions.** *(Lesson 8-12)*

Muir Woods National Monument
is a place to walk and enjoy the
forest. Many of the world's tallest
and oldest redwood trees can be
seen here. This is a map which
shows where trails, camps, and
viewing areas are located.

Use the map. Write the
ordered pair for each place on
the map.

1. Bohemian Grove _____

2. Cathedral Grove _____

3. Visitor Center _____   **4.** Dipsea Trail _____

5. What trail is located at (4, 4)? _____

6. Using the grid, describe one way to get to the Panoramic Trail from
the Parking Area.

_____

_____

Find the volume of each. You may use cubes to help. *(Lesson 8-11)*

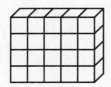

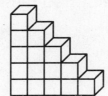

7. _____   **8.** _____

Mixed Review

Find each quotient.

9. 8)24   **10.** 9)45   **11.** 8)48
(7-11)   (7-11)   (7-11)

Name _____

Daily Cumulative Review

Complete. You may use place-value blocks to help. *(Lesson 9-1)*

1. 6 groups of 4

$6 \times \boxed{}$ ones $= \boxed{}$ ones

2. 6 groups of 40

$6 \times \boxed{}$ tens $= \boxed{}$ tens

3. 8×2 tens $= \boxed{}$ tens

$8 \times 20 = \boxed{}$

4. 3×7 tens $= \boxed{}$ tens

$3 \times 70 = \boxed{}$

5. 5×5 tens $= \boxed{}$ tens

$5 \times 50 = \boxed{}$

6. 4×9 tens $= \boxed{}$ tens

$4 \times 90 = \boxed{}$

Solve. You may use a grid to help. *(Lesson 8-12)*

7. Leonard said, "To find the ordered pair (5, 2), I'll go to the right 5 spaces and up 2 spaces." Do you agree or disagree? Explain.

_____

_____

8. What ordered pair is three spaces up from (4, 2)? _____

Mixed Review

Name the shapes of the dotted faces on each solid.

9.
(8-2)

_____

10.
(8-2)

_____

11. How could you take away equal groups to find $3\overline{)15}$?
(7-7)

_____

_____

Daily Cumulative Review

Complete. *(Lesson 9-2)*

1. 6 × 8 ones = ☐ ones

6 × 8 = ☐

2. 6 × 8 tens = ☐ tens

6 × 80 = ☐

3. 6 × 8 hundreds = ☐ hundreds

6 × 800 = ☐

4. 3 × 9 = _____

3 × 90 = _____

3 × 900 = _____

5. 3 × 4 = _____

3 × 40 = _____

3 × 400 = _____

Use place-value blocks to find each product. *(Lesson 9-1)*

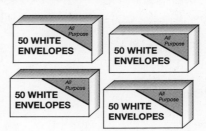

6. How many seeds are in 3 packages?

_____

7. How many envelopes are in 4 boxes?

_____

Mixed Review

Write the name for each.

8.
(8-3)

_____

9.
(8-3)

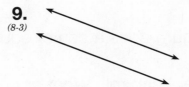

_____

10. What multiplication fact can help you find 30 ÷ 6?
(7-10)

_____

Name _____

Daily Cumulative Review

Estimate each product. *(Lesson 9-3)*

1. 2 × 52 _____

2. 7 × 660 _____

3. 8 × 46 _____

4. 9 × 54 _____

5. 6 × 913 _____

6. 5 × 99 _____

7. 4 × 224 _____

8. 6 × 475 _____

9. Estimate the product of 7 and 84. _____

Find each product using mental math. *(Lesson 9-2)*

10. 4 × 70 = _____

11. 3 × 900 = _____

12. 5 × 60 = _____

13. 9 × 600 = _____

14. 2 × 80 = _____

15. 7 × 50 = _____

Mixed Review

Solve.

16.
(4-12)
$\begin{array}{r} 4,971 \\ -\ 1,643 \\ \hline \end{array}$

17.
(4-12)
$\begin{array}{r} \$9,765 \\ -\ 5,238 \\ \hline \end{array}$

18.
(4-12)
$\begin{array}{r} 2,500 \\ -\ 1,201 \\ \hline \end{array}$

19.
(4-12)
$\begin{array}{r} 3,434 \\ -\ 2,215 \\ \hline \end{array}$

Name the solid figure to answer **20–22**.

20. What solid figure does a basketball look like? _____
(8-1)

21. What solid figure does a can of soup look like? _____
(8-1)

22. I have 1 edge. I can roll. What am I? _____
(8-1)

23. Name 3 two-digit numbers that round to 50 when
(2-8) rounded to the nearest ten.

_____

Daily Cumulative Review

Find each product. You may use place-value blocks or grid paper to help. *(Lesson 9-4)*

1. 3 × 12 = _____

2. 5 × 18 = _____

3. 4 × 23 = _____

4. 2 × 47 = _____

5. 6 × 16 = _____

6. 3 × 13 = _____

7. 6 × 13 = _____

8. 4 × 15 = _____

Estimate to solve each question. *(Lesson 9-3)*

9. Estimate to decide if 4 × 436 is greater than or less than 6 × 226. Explain.

_____

10. The product of 4 and another number is about 120.
Give two numbers that make this sentence true. Explain.

_____

_____

Mixed Review

Write the number of right angles in each polygon.

11.
(8-4)

_____

12.
(8-4)

_____

13.
(8-4)

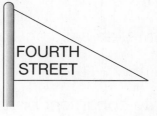

_____

14. Write a number between 1,984 and 2,106.
(2-7)

_____

Name _____

Daily Cumulative Review

Find each product. *(Lesson 9-5)*

1. 1 6
      × 6
     ─────
      3 6
     ☐☐
     ─────
     ☐☐

2.   8 3
      ×   3
     ─────
          ☐
      2 4 0
     ─────
     ☐☐☐

3.   2 1
      ×   8
     ─────
         ☐
     ☐☐☐
     ─────
     ☐☐

4. 1 4
      × 5
     ─────
     ☐☐
     ☐☐
     ─────
     ☐☐

5. $53 \times 4 =$ _____

6. $77 \times 3 =$ _____

7. $19 \times 7 =$ _____

8. $82 \times 6 =$ _____

9. $25 \times 6 =$ _____

10. $15 \times 8 =$ _____

Find the missing number. *(Lesson 9-4)*

11. $19 \times$ _____ $= 57$

12. $14 \times$ _____ $= 98$

12. _____ $\times 4 = 80$

14. _____ $\times 2 = 94$

Mixed Review

Add.

15.
(3-9)
  7 2
  8 1
+   9
─────

16.
(3-9)
  4 1 5
  2 1 2
+   3 6
───────

17.
(3-9)
  7 5 0
  2 8 0
+   5 4
───────

18.
(3-9)
  7 5 5
      5
+ 1 8 8
───────

Write congruent or not congruent for each.

19.
(8-5)

_____

20.
(8-5)

_____

Name _____

Daily Cumulative Review

Find each product. Estimate to check. *(Lesson 9-6)*

1.   4 2
      × 3

2.   8 5
      × 3

3.   5 2
      × 6

4.   1 8
      × 9

5.   3 8
      × 4

6.   5 5
      × 5

7.   7 0
      × 3

8.   2 2
      × 7

9. $71 \times 6 =$ _____

10. $36 \times 4 =$ _____

Solve. *(Lesson 9-5)*

11. Explain why 8×39 is the same as $240 + 72$.

_____

12. Andrea says, "The product of 4 and 54 is greater than 200."
Is she right? Explain.

_____

Mixed Review

Write slide, flip, or turn for each.

13.
(8-5)

14.
(8-5)

_____   _____

15. Is this a multiplication story? Explain.
(5-3)

Mary ran 3 miles a day every day for a week.
How many miles did she run in those 7 days?

_____

Name _____

Daily Cumulative Review

Find each product. Estimate to check. *(Lesson 9-7)*

1.	3 4 2	**2.**	2 8 5	**3.**	7 5 2	**4.**	4 1 8
	× 3		× 3		× 6		× 9

5.	6 3 8	**6.**	1 5 5	**7.**	4 0 7	**8.**	2 2 9
	× 4		× 5		× 3		× 7

9. $3 \times 406 =$ _____   **10.** $336 \times 5 =$ _____

Use any strategy to answer each question. *(Lesson 9-6)*

11. Red blood cells carry oxygen to muscles in our bodies. It takes 60 seconds for a red blood cell to travel all around the body. How long does it take a blood cell travel around the body 5 times?

_____

12. Lisa and her family are driving across the country this summer. The trip will last 21 days. If they stop to see 3 historic sites each day, how many sites will they see during the entire trip?

_____

Mixed Review

Does each object appear to have a line of symmetry?
Write yes or no.

13.
(8-6)

14.
(8-6)

_____   _____

15. Estimate the product of 7 and 42. _____
(9-3)

Name _____

Daily Cumulative Review

Find each product. *(Lesson 9-8)*

| 1. $3.12 × 3 | 2. $2.45 × 3 | 3. $4.78 × 6 | 4. $3.28 × 9 |

| 5. $5.00 × 4 | 6. $1.34 × 5 | 7. $4.17 × 3 | 8. $2.09 × 7 |

9. 6 × $4.16 = _____   **10.** $2.85 × 5 = _____

Use any strategy to answer each question. *(Lesson 9-7)*

11. An elephant's heart beats 30 times each minute. A hummingbird's heart beats about 7 times faster. How many times does the hummingbird's heart beat each minute?

_____

12. If Alan runs 440 yards a day, how many yards will he run in 5 days? _____

13. The Science Club held an exhibition on Wednesday, Thursday, and Friday. Each day 170 people came to see the exhibition. How many people saw the exhibition all together?

_____

Mixed Review

14. Box A has 18 cubes inside. How
(7-14) many cubes are in each box B?

_____

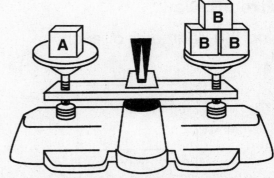

15. Scott has 87 football cards in his collection. He gives fifteen cards to
(8-7) his friend and puts the rest in an album. He places the same number of cards on each page. If he uses 8 pages, how many cards are on each page?

_____

Name _____

Daily Cumulative Review

Find each product using mental math. *(Lesson 9-9)*

1. 53 × 3   **2.** 28 × 2   **3.** 16 × 6   **4.** 33 × 5

_____   _____   _____   _____

5. 41 × 4   **6.** 13 × 2   **7.** 49 × 5   **8.** 62 × 2

_____   _____   _____   _____

9. If you know 40 × 5 = 200, how could you solve 47 × 5 mentally?

_____

Solve. *(Lesson 9-8)*

10. 5 × $3.36 = _____   **11.** $2.83 × 4 = _____

12. A box of floppy disks costs $4.89. How much would 6 boxes of floppy disks cost?

_____

13. A train ticket costs $2.25. Debbie buys a ticket for herself and two friends. How much does she spend?

_____

Mixed Review

Find the perimeter of each.

14.
(8-8)

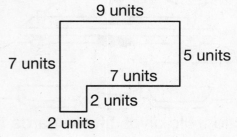

15.
(8-8)

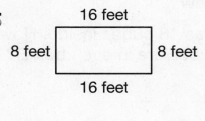

_____   _____

16. Is 250 the same as 25 tens or 25 hundreds? _____
(2-3)

Name _____

Daily Cumulative Review

Use any strategy to solve. *(Lesson 9-10)*

1. George rides his bike to school every day. It takes him 8 minutes to ride 1 mile. How long would it take him to ride 15 miles?

_____

2. Alice rents an apartment for $375 each month. How much will she pay to rent the apartment for 6 months?

_____

3. Kevin can swim 1 lap in 30 seconds. How long would it take to swim 8 laps?

_____

Find each product using mental math. *(Lesson 9-9)*

4. 23×3 **5.** 57×2 **6.** 36×6 **7.** 31×5

_____   _____   _____   _____

8. 19×4 **9.** 56×2 **10.** 42×5 **11.** 64×3

_____   _____   _____   _____

Mixed Review

Continue each pattern.

12. 24, 36, 48, _____, _____, _____
(6-7)

13. 63, 54, 45, _____, _____, _____
(6-7)

Find each quotient.

14. $6\overline{)24}$ **15.** $7\overline{)28}$ **16.** $7\overline{)7}$ **17.** $6\overline{)30}$
(7-10)   (7-10)   (7-10)   (7-10)

18. What multiplication fact can help you find $5\overline{)35}$?
(7-6)

_____

Name _____

Daily Cumulative Review

Complete. *(Lesson 9-11)*

1. 6 ÷ 6 = _____

60 ÷ _____ = 10

_____ ÷ 6 = 100

2. 9 ÷ 3 = _____

_____ ÷ 3 = 30

_____ ÷ 3 = 300

3. 10 ÷ 5 = _____

100 ÷ _____ = 20

_____ ÷ 5 = 200

4. 12 ÷ 2 = _____

_____ ÷ 2 = 60

_____ ÷ 2 = 600

Complete the table to solve the problem. *(Lesson 9-10)*

5. Jerome delivers the school newsletter
5 times each week. How many time does
he deliver the newsletter in one month (4 weeks)? _____

Week	1	2	3	4
Newsletters				

Mixed Review

6. Use grid paper.
(8-9)

   a. Draw a rectangle with a perimeter that measures 18 units.

   b. What is the area of your rectangle?

_____

7. Start with 17 and name the next 5 odd numbers.
(7-12)

_____

8. The sum of two numbers is 80. The numbers are 4 apart.
(3-10) What are they?

_____

Daily Cumulative Review

Estimate each quotient. *(Lesson 9-12)*

1. 25 ÷ 7 _____

2. 30 ÷ 4 _____

3. 17 ÷ 3 _____

4. 21 ÷ 5 _____

5. 61 ÷ 7 _____

6. 13 ÷ 5 _____

7. What basic division fact can you use to help you estimate the quotient of 22 ÷ 7? Explain.

_____

_____

Complete. *(Lesson 9-11)*

8. 6 ÷ 3 = _____

60 ÷ _____ = 30

_____ ÷ 2 = 300

9. 12 ÷ 4 = _____

_____ ÷ 4 = 30

_____ ÷ 4 = 300

10. A carpenter cuts a board 15 feet long into 3 equal pieces. How long is each piece?

_____

Mixed Review

Use any strategy to solve.

11. Drew is planting a garden. He wants to plant equal rows of corn. If
(7-13) Drew has 28 seedlings, what are all the ways to plant the seedlings?

_____

_____

12. Rhonda bought 24 bagels. If there are 6 bagels in
(7-9) each package, how many packages did she buy? _____

13. The school bell rings at 3:15 P.M. It is now
(2-13) 2:50 P.M. How long is it until the bell rings? _____

Daily Cumulative Review

Find each quotient and remainder. You may use counters to help you. *(Lesson 9-13)*

1. 4)19   2. 7)26   3. 5)38

4. 6)57   5. 8)50   6. 4)31

7. 4)23   8. 3)28   9. 7)43

10. Katy says, "If I have 22 apples, I can give myself and 4 friends each 5 apples." Do you agree or disagree?

_____

Use any strategy to solve. *(Lesson 9-12)*

11. You have $17 and need to buy presents for 4 people. You want to spend the money equally. About how much money can you spend on each person?

_____

12. There are 51 tourists visiting a museum. If they are divided into 7 tour groups, about how many are in each group?

_____

Mixed Review

13. What multiplication fact can help you find $63 \div 7$?
(7-10)

_____

14. Is the quotient of $54 \div 9$ greater than, less than, or equal to the
(7-10) quotient of $48 \div 8$? Explain.

_____

Name _____

Daily Cumulative Review

Find each quotient and remainder. *(Lesson 9-14)*

1. 4)18　　　　　**2.** 2)17　　　　　**3.** 4)38

4. 9)80　　　　　**5.** 6)33　　　　　**6.** 8)40

Find each quotient and remainder. *(Lesson 9-13)*

7. 55 ÷ 5 = _____　　**8.** 69 ÷ 7 = _____

9. 42 ÷ 5 = _____　　**10.** 77 ÷ 9 = _____

11. 65 ÷ 7 = _____　　**12.** 51 ÷ 6 = _____

Mixed Review

Continue each pattern.

13. 11, 22, 33, _____, _____, _____
(6-7)

14. 84, 72, 60, _____, _____, _____
(6-7)

15. 30, 60, 90, _____, _____, _____
(6-7)

16. How many corners does a rectangle have? _____
(8-2)

17. How many sides does a circle have? _____
(8-2)

18. How many corners does a triangle have? _____
(8-2)

19. Draw a ray.
(8-3)

Name _____

Daily Cumulative Review

Solve. *(Lesson 9-15)*

You are planning a race. You need a water station every 4 miles.
How many water stations will you need if the race is:

1. 20 miles long? _____

2. 12 miles long? _____

3. 40 miles long? _____

Find each quotient and remainder. *(Lesson 9-14)*

4. 34 ÷ 8 = _____   **5.** 43 ÷ 5 = _____

6. 15 ÷ 2 = _____   **7.** 85 ÷ 9 = _____

Mixed Review

Add. Estimate to check.

8. $6.1 3
(3-15) + 2.6 5

9. $2.9 8
(3-15) + 1.0 6

10. $9.0 1
(3-15) + 1.3 2

11. $4.7 5
(3-15) + 4.7 5

Regroup 1 hundred for 10 tens. You may use place-value
blocks or draw a picture to help.

12. 345 = 2 hundreds, _____ tens, 5 ones
(4-5)

13. 481 = 3 hundreds, _____ tens, 1 one
(4-5)

Use the line graph to answer each question.

14. In what year were the
(1-3) most videos rented? _____

15. In what year were the
(1-3) fewest videos rented? _____

16. In what year were
(1-3) 7,000 videos rented? _____

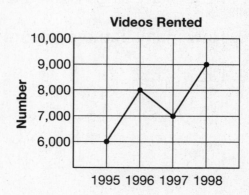

Videos Rented

Name _____

Daily Cumulative Review

Tell how many equal parts. *(Lesson 10-1)*

1.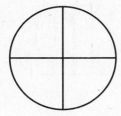

2.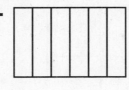

3.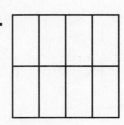

_____   _____   _____

Solve. *(Lesson 9-15)*

4. There are 42 runners in your race. They must be divided into equal starting groups. Find 2 ways to divide 42 runners into equal groups.

a. _____ groups of _____ = 42

b. _____ groups of _____ = 42

Mixed Review

Write each number in standard form.

5. two hundred fifty-two thousand, two _____
(2-4)

6. 300,000 + 40,000 + 200 + 70 _____
(2-4)

Estimate each difference.

7. 774 − 231 _____   **8.** $7.01 − $2.89 _____
(4-4)   (4-4)

Find each product.

9. 4 × 2 = _____   **10.** 5 × 4 = _____   **11.** 2 × 9 = _____
(5-6)   (5-6)   (5-6)

12. What multiplication fact can help you find 54 ÷ 9? _____
(7-11)

Subtract. Check each answer.

13.   5 7 8   **14.**   3 6 1   **15.**   4 2 4   **16.**   9 4 6
(4-10) − 3 9 9   (4-10) − 1 8 9   (4-10) − 2 6 6   (4-10) − 1 6 7

Daily Cumulative Review

Write the fraction of each figure that is shaded. *(Lesson 10-2)*

1.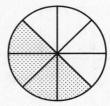

2.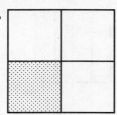

3.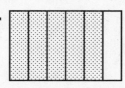

_____   _____   _____

Name the equal parts of each whole. *(Lesson 10-1)*

4.

5.

6.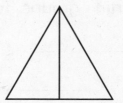

_____   _____   _____

Mixed Review

Solve.

7. How many 3s are in 18? _____
(7-7)

8. How many 4s are in 20? _____
(7-7)

9. Find the sum of 532, 34, and 111. _____
(3-9)

10. If you bought 7 cans of pineapple for 83¢ each, would you spend
(9-8) more than $5.00? Explain.

_____

Use any strategy to solve each problem.

11. Mandy has three stuffed animals she wants to put
(8-7) on a shelf. One stuffed animal is blue, another is
green, and the third is purple. How many different
ways can she arrange the stuffed animals if she
wants the purple one in the middle?   _____

Name _____

Name _____

Name _____

Daily Cumulative Review

Complete. You may use fraction strips to help. *(Lesson 10-3)*

1. $\frac{1}{6} = \frac{\square}{12}$

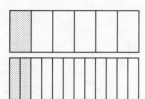
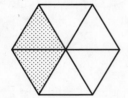

2. $\frac{4}{5} = \frac{\square}{10}$

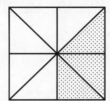

3. $\frac{2}{3} = \frac{\square}{6}$

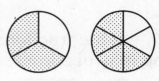

Write the fraction of each figure that is shaded. *(Lesson 10-2)*

4.

5.

6.

_____   _____   _____

Mixed Review

Look for a pattern. What are the next three numbers?

7. 20, 40, 60, 80, _____, _____, _____
(1-11)

8. 170, 145, 120, 95, _____, _____, _____
(1-11)

9. Three students are waiting in line to
(2-5) turn in their paper. Ken is in front of
Skip. Trevor is last in line. In what
order are the students standing? _____

10. Write the total value in dollars and cents. _____
(3-13)

Daily Cumulative Review

**Place the fractions in order from greatest to least.
You may use fraction strips to help.** *(Lesson 10-4)*

1. $\frac{1}{2}, \frac{5}{6}, \frac{1}{4}$ _____

2. $\frac{3}{5}, \frac{1}{4}, \frac{2}{6}$ _____

**Write if the fractions are equivalent or not equivalent.
You may use fraction strips to help.** *(Lesson 10-3)*

3.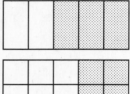

4.

5.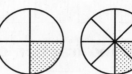

_____   _____   _____

Mixed Review

Order from least to greatest.

6. 564, 654, 456 _____
(2-7)

7. 3,643, 3,336; 3,463; _____
(2-7)

8. Complete the table. Write the rule.
(1-6)

In	15	32	26	19	40	23
Out	8	25	19			

Rule: _____

9. Alicia bought three items at the store.
(3-10) She spent $14. What did Alicia buy?
Use the prices in the table to solve.

Item	Cost
Notebook	$5
Colored Pencils	$2
Calculator	$8
Paper	$1

_____

_____

_____

Name _____

Daily Cumulative Review

Estimate the amount that is shaded. *(Lesson 10-5)*

1.

2.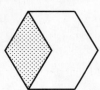

3.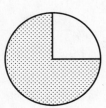

_____ _____ _____

_____ _____ _____

Compare. Write <, >, or =. You may use fraction strips to help. *(Lesson 10-4)*

4. $\frac{1}{4}$ ◯ $\frac{2}{6}$

5. $\frac{2}{3}$ ◯ $\frac{2}{4}$

6. $\frac{1}{2}$ ◯ $\frac{3}{6}$

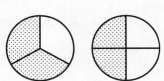

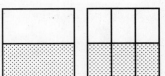

Mixed Review

Solve. Check each answer.

7.
(4-12)
$$\begin{array}{r} 4,500 \\ -\ 2,900 \\ \hline \end{array}$$

8.
(4-12)
$$\begin{array}{r} 1,456 \\ -\ 876 \\ \hline \end{array}$$

9.
(4-12)
$$\begin{array}{r} 7,876 \\ -\ 2,390 \\ \hline \end{array}$$

10.
(4-12)
$$\begin{array}{r} 3,333 \\ -\ 1,993 \\ \hline \end{array}$$

Find the area of each.

11.
(8-9)
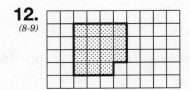

12.
(8-9)

_____ _____

13. Find the product of 8, 6, and 0. _____
(6-8)

Daily Cumulative Review

Write a fraction to tell what part of each set is circled.
(Lesson 10-6)

1.    **2.**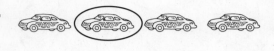

_____   _____

Estimate the amount that is shaded. *(Lesson 10-5)*

3.    **4.** 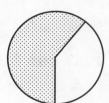   **5.**

_____   _____   _____

_____   _____   _____

Mixed Review

Write each time two ways. Write A.M. or P.M.

6.
(2-12)
 School
Starts

7.
(2-12)
 Lunch
Time

_____   _____

_____   _____

8. Give three ways to make 77 cents.
(3-12)

_____

_____

_____

126

Daily Cumulative Review

Complete. *(Lesson 10-7)*

1. To find $\frac{1}{6}$ of 12 divide 12 into _____ equal groups.

2. To find $\frac{1}{4}$ of 24 divide 24 into _____ equal groups.

Write a fraction to tell what part of each set is circled.
(Lesson 10-6)

3.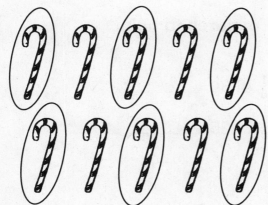

4.

_____   _____

Mixed Review

5. What is the pattern for multiples of 11?
(6-7)

_____

6. What multiplication fact can help you find 72 ÷ 8? _____
(7-11)

Complete the table.

	Number	100 More	100 Less
7. *(2-3)*	4,753		
8. *(2-3)*	6,299		
9. *(2-3)*	7,101		

10. Write a number between 4,918 and 5,006. _____
(2-7)

Daily Cumulative Review

Write a mixed number for each. *(Lesson 10-8)*

1.

_____

2.

_____

Solve. You may use counters or draw pictures to help.
(Lesson 10-7)

3. $\frac{1}{3}$ of 18 _____

4. $\frac{1}{6}$ of 30 _____

5. $\frac{1}{8}$ of 32 _____

6. $\frac{1}{5}$ of 25 _____

Mixed Review

Find each sum using mental math.

7. $\$40 + \$30 =$ _____
(3-1)

8. $200 + 500 =$ _____
(3-1)

9. $100 + 800 =$ _____
(3-1)

10. $\$50 + \$40 =$ _____
(3-1)

11. Courtney is putting dolls on her shelves. She has 4 shelves that will
(9-13) each hold 7 dolls. Courtney has 32 dolls. How many will not fit on
the shelves?

_____

12. Sarah multiplied $3.45 and 6. She recorded $2,070. Is she correct?
(9-8)

_____

13. Thompson has 3 shirts, one orange, one blue and one green. He has
(7-13) 2 pairs of pants, one black pair and one tan pair. What are all the
combinations of shirts and pants he could wear?

_____

_____

Name _____

Daily Cumulative Review

Find each sum or difference. You may use fraction strips or draw a picture to help. *(Lesson 10-9)*

1. $\frac{11}{12} - \frac{8}{12} =$ _____

2. $\frac{4}{7} - \frac{3}{7} =$ _____

3. $\frac{1}{3} + \frac{1}{3} =$ _____

4. $\frac{3}{12} + \frac{5}{12} =$ _____

Write a mixed number for each. *(Lesson 10-8)*

5.

_____

6.

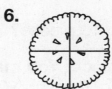

_____

Mixed Review

Add.

7.
(3-9)
```
    5 6
  2 1 3
+ 1 6 0
```

8.
(3-9)
```
  3 4 5
    2 3
+ 2 4 4
```

9.
(3-9)
```
  1 2 1
  2 0 0
+   8 7
```

10.
(3-9)
```
  6 5 2
      8
+   7 3
```

11. What is 569 minus 389? _____
(4-9)

12. How many thousands is 100,000? How many ten thousands?
(2-4)

_____

13. To compare 5,743 and 5,421 you should look at the digits in the
(2-6)

_____ place.

Daily Cumulative Review

Solve. *(Lesson 10-10)*

Your group won the class book reading contest! Your group is having a party after lunch and there are 6 students to feed.

You want at least 3 brownies per student. How many pans of brownies will you need if...

1. each pan is cut into 6 pieces? _____

2. each pan is cut into 8 pieces? _____

3. each pan is cut into 10 pieces? _____

Find each sum or difference. You may use fraction strips or draw a picture to help. *(Lesson 10-9)*

4. $\frac{5}{9} - \frac{3}{9} =$ _____

5. $\frac{5}{11} + \frac{5}{11} =$ _____

Mixed Review

Find each product.

6. $(0 \times 5) \times 7$
(6-8)

7. $(4 \times 2) \times 6$
(6-8)

8. $4 \times (3 \times 1)$
(6-8)

_____   _____   _____

9. How could you use mental math to find $1,300 - 800$?
(4-12)

_____

Write slide, flip, or turn for each.

10.
(8-5)
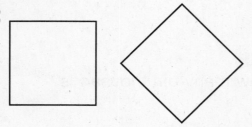

11.
(8-5)
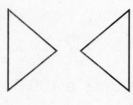

_____   _____

Name _____

Daily Cumulative Review

Estimate each length. Then measure to the nearest inch.
(Lesson 10-11)

1.    _____

2.    _____

Solve. *(Lesson 10-10)*

Your team won the school talent contest! Your team is
having a party after school and there are 5 students to feed.

You want at least 3 glasses of pop per student. How many
bottles of pop will you need if...

3. each bottle holds 6 glasses of pop? _____

4. each bottle holds 4 glasses of pop? _____

5. each bottle holds 10 glasses of pop? _____

Mixed Review

Write odd or even for each. You may use color cubes to help.

6. 6 _____   **7.** 1 _____   **8.** 20 _____
(7-12)   *(7-12)*   *(7-12)*

Find each quotient.

9. 64 ÷ 8 = _____   **10.** 16 ÷ 8 = _____
(7-11)   *(7-11)*

11. 54 ÷ 9 = _____   **12.** 27 ÷ 9 = _____
(7-11)   *(7-11)*

Use any strategy to solve.

13. The sum of two numbers is 53. The
(3-10) numbers are 7 apart. What are they? _____

14. Write any 5 numbers less than 700 that round to 700
(2-9) when you round to the nearest 100.

_____

Daily Cumulative Review

Measure the length of each object to the nearest $\frac{1}{2}$ inch.
(Lesson 10-12)

1.

_____

2.

_____

Estimate each length. Then measure to the nearest inch.
(Lesson 10-11)

3.

_____

4.

_____

Mixed Review

Find each product.

5.
(9-8)
$$\begin{array}{r} \$1.5\,4 \\ \times \quad 2 \\ \hline \end{array}$$

6.
(9-8)
$$\begin{array}{r} \$2.6\,2 \\ \times \quad 3 \\ \hline \end{array}$$

7.
(9-8)
$$\begin{array}{r} \$6.1\,1 \\ \times \quad 4 \\ \hline \end{array}$$

8.
(9-8)
$$\begin{array}{r} \$0.3\,2 \\ \times \quad 8 \\ \hline \end{array}$$

9. Write two addends with a sum of 342.
(3-7)

_____

10. Use the fewest coins to make 56 cents.
(3-12)

_____

_____

Daily Cumulative Review

Write each measurement in inches. *(Lesson 10-13)*

1. 5 feet 8 inches

2. 1 foot 7 inches

3. 4 feet 11 inches

_____   _____   _____

Measure the length of each object to the nearest $\frac{1}{4}$ inch.
(Lesson 10-12)

4.

5.

_____   _____

Mixed Review

6. Complete the tally table.
(1-7)

Number of televisions in the homes of Mr. Couch's third grade class:

2, 3, 1, 1, 1, 2, 2, 3, 2, 2, 2, 1, 1, 1, 1, 1, 1, 1, 2, 2, 3, 3, 1, 1, 1, 1

TVs	Tally	Number
1	卌 卌 IIII	
2		
3		

Write whether each angle is a right angle, less than a right angle, or greater than a right angle.

7.
(8-4)

8.
(8-4)

9.
(8-4)

_____   _____   _____

10. Missy said, "I lost a coin! I had $9.63. Now I
(3-13) only have 1 five-dollar bill, 4 one-dollar bills, 2 quarters, 1 nickel and 3 pennies." What coin did Missy lose?

_____

Name _____

Daily Cumulative Review

Compare. Write <, >, or =. *(Lesson 10-14)*

1. 2 feet ◯ 30 inches

2. 4 miles ◯ 5,280 yards

3. 6 feet ◯ 2 yards

4. 2 yards ◯ 84 inches

Write each measurement in inches. *(Lesson 10-13)*

5. 7 feet 2 inches

6. 3 feet 5 inches

7. 6 feet 4 inches

_____   _____   _____

Mixed Review

Add.

8.
(3-8)
$$5,681 + 2,219$$

9.
(3-8)
$$3,333 + 5,222$$

10.
(3-8)
$$5,600 + 1,400$$

11.
(3-8)
$$\$6,800 + 1,200$$

Subtract.

12.
(4-12)
$$7,621 - 3,342$$

13.
(4-12)
$$9,909 - 3,058$$

14.
(4-12)
$$5,432 - 4,932$$

15.
(4-12)
$$\$5,743 - 1,563$$

Multiply.

16. $3 \times 7 =$ _____
(6-1)

17. $9 \times 3 =$ _____
(6-1)

18. $3 \times 3 =$ _____
(6-1)

Divide.

19. $21 \div 7 =$ _____
(7-10)

20. $36 \div 6 =$ _____
(7-10)

21. $49 \div 7 =$ _____
(7-10)

Write the name for each.

22.
(8-3)
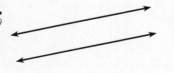

23.
(8-3)
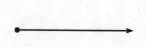

24.
(8-3)

_____   _____   _____

Name _____

Daily Cumulative Review

Use logical reasoning to solve. *(Lesson 10-15)*

1. Help Dana figure out which teams finished in first, second, third, and fourth place. The Panthers finished in last place. The Cougars finished in third place. The Lions beat the Cougars and the Jaguars.

_____

2. Mindy, Megan, Marty, and Melissa are all brothers and sisters. Melissa is the oldest. Mindy is 13 years old. Marty is older than Megan. If each person is either 7, 10, 13, or 14 years old, how old is each person?

_____

Compare. Write $<$, $>$, or $=$. *(Lesson 10-14)*

3. 3 ft $\bigcirc$ 36 in.

4. 1 mi $\bigcirc$ 6 yd

5. 10,000 ft $\bigcirc$ 2 mi

6. 2 yd $\bigcirc$ 70 in.

Mixed Review

Find each product.

7. $(3 \times 0) \times 6$
(6-8)

8. $(3 \times 4) \times 2$
(6-8)

9. $(2 \times 6) \times 3$
(6-8)

_____   _____   _____

Solve. Check each answer.

10. $\begin{array}{r} 584 \\ -\ 195 \end{array}$
(4-10)

11. $\begin{array}{r} 602 \\ -\ 43 \end{array}$
(4-11)

12. $\begin{array}{r} \$4,834 \\ -\ 2,476 \end{array}$
(4-12)

13. $\begin{array}{r} 8,100 \\ -\ 3,500 \end{array}$
(4-12)

14. What multiplication fact can help you find $45 \div 9$? _____
(7-11)

Solve. Use any strategy.

15. You want to send invitations to 27 people. The invitations you want come in packages of 8. How many packages will you need?
(6-9)

_____

Name _____

Daily Cumulative Review

Write the fraction and the decimal to name each shaded part. *(Lesson 11-1)*

1.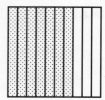

2.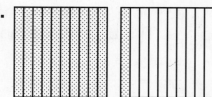

_____   _____

Use logical reasoning to solve. *(Lesson 10-15)*

3. Rosa has 6 coins. The total value of the coins is $0.75. She doesn't have any pennies or nickels. What coins does Rosa have?

_____

Mixed Review

Round to the nearest ten.

4. 56 _____
(2-8)

5. 111 _____
(2-8)

6. 439 _____
(2-8)

Write the total value in cents.

7.
(3-12)  _____

8.
(3-12)  _____

Use the bar graph to answer the questions.

9. Which season was the least favorite?
(1-2)

_____

10. Which season did 12 students vote for?
(1-2)

_____

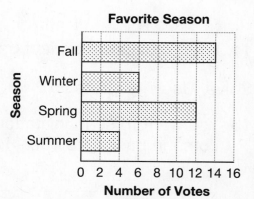

Favorite Season

Season

Fall
Winter
Spring
Summer

0 2 4 6 8 10 12 14 16
Number of Votes

Daily Cumulative Review

Write each as a decimal. *(Lesson 11-2)*

1. sixteen hundredths _____

2. two and four hundredths _____

3. $\frac{98}{100}$ _____

4. $1\frac{24}{100}$ _____

Write each as a decimal. *(Lesson 11-1)*

5. three tenths _____

6. $\frac{8}{10}$ _____

7. one and five tenths _____

8. $2\frac{2}{10}$ _____

Mixed Review

Use front-end estimation to estimate each sum.

9. *(3-16)*
$$\begin{array}{r} \$7.32 \\ +\ 2.45 \\ \hline \end{array}$$

10. *(3-16)*
$$\begin{array}{r} 667 \\ 239 \\ +\ 431 \\ \hline \end{array}$$

11. *(3-16)*
$$\begin{array}{r} 568 \\ 360 \\ +\ 124 \\ \hline \end{array}$$

12. *(3-16)*
$$\begin{array}{r} \$4.67 \\ 2.56 \\ +\ 3.99 \\ \hline \end{array}$$

Name the solid figure that each object looks like.

13. *(8-1)*

14. *(8-1)*

15. *(8-1)*

_____

_____

_____

Write a number sentence for each. Then solve.

16. *(4-1)* Karl had a math test today. There were 18 questions on the test. Karl missed 7 problems on the test. How many did he get correct?

_____

17. *(4-1)* Heather has $15. She buys a t-shirt for $11. How much money does she have left?

_____

Daily Cumulative Review

Find each sum or difference. You may use tenths grids to help. *(Lesson 11-3)*

1. 4.4	**2.** 2.3	**3.** 8.5	**4.** 0.9
+ 2.5	+ 4.8	− 4.7	− 0.4

What is the value of each bold digit? *(Lesson 11-2)*

5. 0.**5**6 _____

6. **3**.27 _____

7. 2.6**9** _____

Mixed Review

Find the perimeter of each.

8.
(8-8)

8 in.

3 in.   3 in.

8 in.

9.
(8-8)

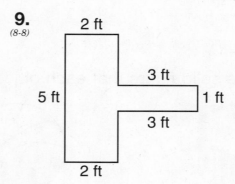

_____   _____

Find each product.

10. $3 \times 9 =$ _____
(6-1)

11. $6 \times 0 =$ _____
(5-7)

12. $7 \times 7 =$ _____
(6-4)

Write each time in two ways.

13.
(2-11)

14.
(2-11)

_____   _____

Name _____

Daily Cumulative Review

Write each as a money amount. *(Lesson 11-4)*

1. $\frac{56}{100}$ of $1.00 _____

2. $2\frac{76}{100}$ of $1.00 _____

3. six dollars and fourteen cents

4. two and forty-three hundredths of $1.00

_____   _____

Find each sum or difference. You may use tenths grids to help. *(Lesson 11-3)*

5.   5.6
      $+ \ 3.7$

6.   0.9
      $+ \ 1.9$

7.   5.3
      $- \ 2.5$

8.   1.5
      $- \ 0.7$

Mixed Review

Estimate each sum or difference.

9. $479 + $213 _____
(3-4)

10. 572 − 321 _____
(4-4)

11. $9.12 − $2.67 _____
(4-4)

12. 68 + 14 _____
(3-4)

Use any strategy to solve.

13. The sum of two numbers is 85. The numbers
(3-10) are 13 apart. What are they?   _____

14. What is the product of 4 and 7? _____
(6-2)

15. What is the product of 5 and 3? _____
(6-1)

16. Complete the table.
(2-2)

Number	Number of Ones	Number of Tens	Number of Hundreds
600			6
900	900		
1,300		130	13

Daily Cumulative Review

Solve. *(Lesson 11-5)*

You have decided to purchase a birthday gift for a cousin. You want to go to the Specialty Store to buy the gift. You have to be home by 4:30 P.M. for soccer practice. Below is a copy of the bus schedule for the bus which you will take. The bus stops at Linsey Ave. right outside your house.

Leave Linsey Ave.	Arrive at Specialty Store	Leave Specialty Store	Arrive Linsey Ave.
1:30 P.M.	2:00 P.M.	3:15 P.M.	3:45 P.M.
2:30 P.M.	3:00 P.M.	3:45 P.M.	4:15 P.M.

1. When is the latest time you could leave the Specialty Store in order to get home on time? _____

2. How long does it take the bus to get to the Specialty Store from your bus stop on Linsey Ave.? _____

Write each as a money amount. *(Lesson 11-4)*

3. $\frac{23}{100}$ of $1.00 _____

4. $2\frac{3}{100}$ of $1.00 _____

5. three dollars and sixty-eight cents

6. ninety-seven hundredths of $1.00

_____

_____

Mixed Review

Compare. Use $<$, $>$, or $=$.

7. 5,689 ◯ 6,789
(2-6)

8. 3,473 ◯ 3,473
(2-6)

Add. Estimate to check.

9.   66
(3-6) $+\ 57$

10. $78
(3-6) $+\ 53$

11. 682
(3-7) $+\ 230$

12. $521
(3-7) $+\ 111$

Daily Cumulative Review

Estimate the length of each object. Then measure to the nearest centimeter. *(Lesson 11-6)*

1.

2.

estimate _____   estimate _____

actual _____   actual _____

Solve. *(Lesson 11-5)*

You want to purchase a gift for Mother's Day. You are bringing $15.00 with you to the local gift shop.

3. If a one-way bus fare is $0.75, how much
spending money do you actually have?   _____

4. You buy an earring set. It costs $12.30. How
much money do you have left over to buy
a snack? (Don't forget about the bus fare!)   _____

5. **a.** A soft pretzel costs $0.55. Do you have
enough money to buy one for your snack?   _____

b. Could you buy two soft pretzels?   _____

Mixed Review

Use mental math to find each product.

6. 400 ÷ 2 = _____
(9-11)

7. 420 ÷ 6 = _____
(9-11)

8. What is the greatest possible sum using three of these numbers?
(3-9)

| 67 | 632 | 398 | 129 | 800 |

_____

9. Find the difference of 60 and 24. _____
(4-7)

Daily Cumulative Review

Match each with its estimate. *(Lesson 11-7)*

1. width of a hallway at school _____

2. width of a piece of notebook paper _____

3. length of a bike ride _____

a. 20 cm

b. 3 km

c. 3 m

Choose the best estimate for each. *(Lesson 11-6)*

4.

a. 6 cm _____

b. 1 dm

5.

a. 6 cm _____

b. 1 dm

Mixed Review

6. If the pattern continues, which shape should come next?
(1-11)

       _____

7. Carla wants to exercise for twenty-five minutes. If she starts at
(2-13) 4:45 P.M., what time should she stop?

_____

8. Each pizza serves 12 people. How many pizzas
(6-9) will you need to serve 84 people? _____

9. Suppose a salad serves 4 people. How many
(9-14) salads will you need to serve 22 people? _____

Daily Cumulative Review

Use any strategy to solve. *(Lesson 11-8)*

1. You and your friends are playing a board game. You are on the sixth space. You go forward 9 spaces, then backward 5 spaces. Then you go forward 6 spaces and back 2. On what space are you now?

_____

2. You have 14 marbles. You trade 6 of your marbles for 9 of your friend's marbles. Then you lose some marbles so you have 11. How many marbles did you lose?

_____

Write whether you would measure each in cm, m, or km. *(Lesson 11-7)*

3. distance to the lunch room _____

4. width across the state _____

5. length of your finger _____

Mixed Review

Add.

6.
(3-8)
$$6,783 + 2,490$$

7.
(3-8)
$$2,389 + 1,501$$

8.
(3-8)
$$4,009 + 3,991$$

9.
(3-8)
$$3,931 + 999$$

Solve. You may use counters or draw a picture to help.

10. Find $\frac{1}{4}$ of 28. _____
(10-7)

11. Find $\frac{1}{5}$ of 35. _____
(10-7)

12. Find $\frac{1}{2}$ of 18. _____
(10-7)

13. Find $\frac{1}{3}$ of 18. _____
(10-7)

14. There are 24 students in your class. They must be divided into equal
(9-15) groups. Find 3 different ways to divide 24 students into equal groups.

a. _____ groups of _____ = 24

b. _____ groups of _____ = 24

c. _____ groups of _____ = 24

Daily Cumulative Review

Circle the best estimate for each. *(Lesson 12-1)*

1.

    a. 1 cup

    b. 1 quart

    c. 1 gallon

2.

    a. 1 cup

    b. 1 pint

    c. 1 quart

3.

    a. 1 pint

    b. 1 quart

    c. 1 cup

Use any strategy to solve. *(Lesson 11-8)*

4. A shelf at the store had 18 bottles of apple juice on it. One shopper buys 4 bottles, and another buys 3 bottles. The stock person restocks the shelf with 12 more bottles Then 4 more shoppers each buy 3 bottles. How many bottles of apple juice are on the shelf?

_____

5. Shelly rode the elevator and got off on the fourth floor. She then climbed up 3 flights of stairs and got back on the elevator. She took the elevator down 6 floors. What floor is she on now?

_____

Mixed Review

6. Use the data in the table. Complete the pictograph.

(1-8) **a.**

Where Students Like to Read	
At a desk	╫╫ ╫╫
At a library	╫╫
On the floor	╫╫ IIII
On the bed	╫╫ ╫╫ II
Other	IIII

Where Students Like to Read	
At a desk	✶ ✶ ✶ ✶ ✶
At a library	
On the floor	
On the bed	
Other	

✶ = 2 students

    b. Suppose each symbol in the pictograph above represented 4 students. How many symbols would there be for "other"?

_____

Daily Cumulative Review

Circle the better estimate for each. *(Lesson 12-2)*

1.

   a. 2 mL

   b. 2 L

2.

   a. 591 mL

   b. 591 L

3.

   a. 3 mL

   b. 3 L

Compare. Use <, >, or =. *(Lesson 12-1)*

4. 20 cups $\bigcirc$ 10 pints

5. 2 gallons $\bigcirc$ 6 quarts

6. 6 pints $\bigcirc$ 1 gallon

7. 8 cups $\bigcirc$ 3 quarts

Mixed Review

Write congruent or not congruent for each.

8.
(8-5)

_____

9.
(8-5)

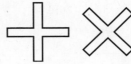

_____

Write the value of each underlined digit.

10. <u>3</u>3,496 _____
(2-4)

11. 457,<u>2</u>19 _____
(2-4)

12. <u>9</u>62,058 _____
(2-4)

Write which operation you would use. Then solve.

13. Lane bought a bag of marshmallows for $1.23 and bunch of bananas
(7-9) for $1.57. How much money did he spend?

_____

Name _____

Daily Cumulative Review

Compare. Use <, >, or =. *(Lesson 12-3)*

1. 5 ounces ◯ 1 pound

2. 20 ounces ◯ 1 pound

3. 1 ounce ◯ 1 pound

4. 16 ounces ◯ 1 pound

Circle the better estimate for each. *(Lesson 12-2)*

5.

a. 2 mL

b. 2 L

6.

a. 250 mL

b. 250 L

7.

a. 1 mL

b. 1 L

Mixed Review

Use the calendar to answer each question.

8. What day of the week
(2-14) is the 14th?

_____

9. How many Tuesdays are
(2-14) in the month shown?

_____

April						
Sun	Mon	Tue	Wed	Thu	Fri	Sat
		1	2	3	4	5
6	7	8	9	10	11	12
13	14	15	16	17	18	19
20	21	22	23	24	25	26
27	28	29	30			

10. Suppose Melinda wants to order 30 paintbrushes for her art class.
(2-5) She can buy brushes in packages of 3 or 6. How many ways could
she order exactly 30 brushes?

a. List all the possible ways she could order 30 paintbrushes.

Packages of 3					
Packages of 6					

b. How many ways are there? _____

Name _____

Daily Cumulative Review

Circle the best estimate for each. *(Lesson 12-4)*

1.

a. 1 g
b. 1 kg

2.

a. 10 g
b. 10 kg

3.

a. 10 g
b. 10 kg

Write whether each is less or more than a pound. *(Lesson 12-3)*

4.

5.

6.

_____   _____   _____

Mixed Review

Find each product.

7.
(6-1)
$$\begin{array}{r} 3 \\ \times\, 2 \\ \hline \end{array}$$

8.
(6-1)
$$\begin{array}{r} 7 \\ \times\, 3 \\ \hline \end{array}$$

9.
(6-2)
$$\begin{array}{r} 4 \\ \times\, 4 \\ \hline \end{array}$$

10.
(6-2)
$$\begin{array}{r} 5 \\ \times\, 4 \\ \hline \end{array}$$

11.
(6-3)
$$\begin{array}{r} 6 \\ \times\, 8 \\ \hline \end{array}$$

12.
(6-3)
$$\begin{array}{r} 9 \\ \times\, 6 \\ \hline \end{array}$$

Subtract.

13.
(4-15)
$$\begin{array}{r} \$4\,0.0\,0 \\ -\quad 8.3\,9 \\ \hline \end{array}$$

14.
(4-15)
$$\begin{array}{r} \$4.8\,9 \\ -\ 1.9\,3 \\ \hline \end{array}$$

15.
(4-15)
$$\begin{array}{r} \$3\,0.0\,0 \\ -\ 1\,5.8\,7 \\ \hline \end{array}$$

16.
(4-15)
$$\begin{array}{r} \$6.2\,3 \\ -\ 6.1\,3 \\ \hline \end{array}$$

17. Makena has 12 pieces of gum. She can give 3 to each of her cousins.
(7-3) How many cousins are in her family?

_____

Daily Cumulative Review

Write the temperature using °C or °F. *(Lesson 12-5)*

1.
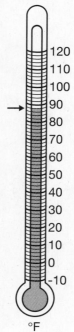
°F

2.
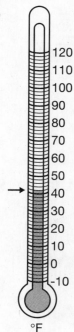
°F

3.
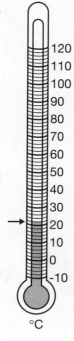
°C

_____ _____ _____

Circle the best estimate for each. *(Lesson 12-4)*

4.
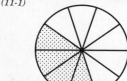

a. 1 g

b. 1 kg

5.
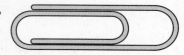

a. 15 g

b. 15 kg

6.

a. 1 g

b. 1 kg

Mixed Review

7. Write each part of the circle as a fraction and a decimal.
(11-1)

		Fraction	Decimal
a.	Shaded		
b.	Not shaded		

Daily Cumulative Review

Solve. *(Lesson 12-6)*

You are going on a biking trip. This is what you plan to take:

Item	Weight
Backpack	3 lb
1 camera	1 lb 8 oz
1 canteen of water	2 lb 8 oz
1 repair kit	8 oz
1 first aid kit	8 oz
1 jacket	8 oz

1. What will the total weight of your backpack be when you pack all of these items?

_____

2. What would the total weight of your backpack be when you pack all these items and another canteen of water?

_____

Circle the better estimate for each. *(Lesson 12-5)*

3.

    a. 0°C

    b. 0°F

4.

    a. 92°C

    b. 92°F

5.

    a. 70°C

    b. 70°F

Mixed Review

Find the volume of each shape. You may use cubes to help.

6.
(8-11)

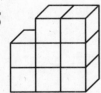

7.
(8-11)

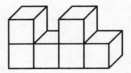

_____   _____

Name _____

Daily Cumulative Review

Write whether each is impossible, possible, or certain.
(Lesson 12-7)

1. The sun will rise in the morning. _____

2. Summer's high temperatures will
   arrive earlier than usual. _____

3. A mouse will become President of the United States. _____

Solve. *(Lesson 12-6)*

You are going on a camping trip. This is what you plan to take:

Item	Weight
backpack	3 lb
2 sweaters	1 lb each
3 canteens of water	2 lb 8 oz each
2 flashlights	8 oz each
1 sleeping bag	5 lb
1 first aid kit	8 oz
socks, t-shirts, etc.	3 lb

4. What will the total weight of your backpack
   be when you pack all of these items? _____

5. If you could carry 5 lb more, what would you include? (Estimate the
   weight of the item if it is not on the list.)

_____

Mixed Review

Find each product.

6. (5-5)
$$\begin{array}{r} 5 \\ \times\,4 \\ \hline \end{array}$$

7. (5-5)
$$\begin{array}{r} 6 \\ \times\,5 \\ \hline \end{array}$$

8. (5-5)
$$\begin{array}{r} 3 \\ \times\,5 \\ \hline \end{array}$$

9. (5-5)
$$\begin{array}{r} 9 \\ \times\,5 \\ \hline \end{array}$$

Write whether each has equal parts or unequal parts.

10. (10-1) 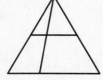 _____

11. (10-1) _____

Daily Cumulative Review

Suppose you put these cubes in a bag. Predict which cubes you are more likely to pull out. *(Lesson 12-8)*

1.

_____

2.

_____

Write whether each is likely or unlikely. *(Lesson 12-7)*

3. You will find a diamond ring today. _____

4. You will brush your teeth today. _____

5. You will have homework this week. _____

Mixed Review

6. Continue the pattern. Then write the rule.
(4-2)

In	170	180	190	200	210	220
Out	130	140	150			

Rule: _____

7. Kathleen is saving money to buy a CD player.
(9-10) The first week she saves $2. The second week she saves $4. The third week she saves $6. If this pattern continues, how many more weeks will it be until she has saved $56 in all? _____

8. Maurice buys buys 5 tickets to the game. Each
(9-8) ticket costs $6.55. How much does Maurice spend? _____

9. 16 painters will paint 4 walls. How many painters
(9-14) should work on each wall? _____

Daily Cumulative Review

Complete to show each probability. *(Lesson 12-9)*

1.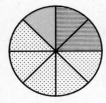

a. grey: ☐ out of 8 or $\frac{☐}{8}$

b. striped: ☐ out of 8 or $\frac{☐}{8}$

c. dotted: ☐ out of 8 or $\frac{☐}{8}$

2.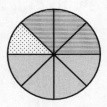

a. grey: ☐ out of 8 or $\frac{☐}{8}$

b. striped: ☐ out of 8 or $\frac{☐}{8}$

c. dotted: ☐ out of 8 or $\frac{☐}{8}$

Suppose you put these cubes in a bag. Predict which cubes you are more likely to pull out. *(Lesson 12-8)*

3.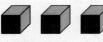

_____

4.

_____

Mixed Review

Is each line a line of symmetry? Write yes or no.

5.
(8-6)

_____

6.
(8-6)

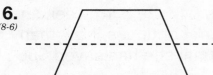

_____

Daily Cumulative Review

Write whether each spinner is fair or unfair. *(Lesson 12-10)*

1.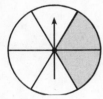

2.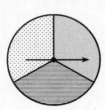

_____   _____

Use probability to solve. *(Lesson 12-9)*

3. 2 sides of a cube are red, 3 sides are blue, and 1 side is yellow.

   a. If you toss the cube, which color
     is most likely to land face up? _____

   b. If you toss the cube, which color
     is least likely to land face up? _____

Mixed Review

Find each missing number. You may use a hundred chart to help.

4. 61 − _____ = 20   **5.** 45 − _____ = 17
(4-3)   *(4-3)*

6. _____ − 19 = 49   **7.** _____ − 27 = 38
(4-3)   *(4-3)*

8. Kaley decides she wants to serve slices of peaches with each bowl of
(6-5) ice cream. She needs 4 slices for each bowl. How many slices does
    she need for:

   a. 5 bowls of ice cream? _____

   b. 7 bowls of ice cream? _____

   c. 9 bowls of ice cream? _____

9. You are making cake for a party. Each cake has 8 pieces.
(6-9)

   a. If 76 people will be at the party, how many cakes
     should you make so that each person gets one piece? _____

   b. How many pieces will be left over? _____